666/

D1631575

PORTSMOUTH POLYTECHNIC LIBRARY

AUTHOR HENRY. E.C.

TITLE ELECTRONIC
CERAMICS.

ACCESSION NUMBER
7044043

LOCATION

CLASS NUMBER
666 . HEN

ELECTRONIC CERAMICS

WITHDRAWN
UNIVERSITY OF
PORTSMOUTH LIBRARY

The *Chemistry in Action Series* has been designed to give the interested layman a thorough introduction to the many different sides of the chemical industry. Prepared under the joint supervision of the Education Activities Committee of the Manufacturing Chemists' Association and Doubleday & Company, Inc., each volume focuses on a particular segment of the chemical industry and relates the pure chemical science to the final products met in everyday life. The volumes have each been written by distinguished authorities in the field, and cover such various fields as agricultural chemistry, chemicals from the atmosphere and from the ocean, and the chemistry of paints, the soil, water purification, sulphuric acid, the silicon compounds, synthetic textiles, drugs, and antibiotics.

WITHDRAWN
UNIVERSITY OF
PORTSMOUTH LIBRARY

Edward C. Henry is a Consulting Engineer at the Space Sciences Laboratory of the General Electric Company, located at the company's Valley Forge Space Technology Center, King of Prussia, Pennsylvania. He has a B.S. degree from Rutgers, M.S. from the University of Nevada, and Ph.D. and Cer.E. degrees from Pennsylvania State University. He is a Registered Professional Engineer in the states of Pennsylvania and New York.

Dr. Henry engaged in university teaching and research for twenty-three years, the last eight years of which he was Professor of Ceramics and Chairman of the Department of Ceramics at Penn State. He then pursued investigations in the field of electronic ceramics at the Electronics Laboratory of the General Electric Company, Electronics Park, Syracuse, New York, from 1953 to 1965, before transferring to the Space Sciences Laboratory.

Dr. Henry was President of the National Institute of Ceramic Engineers in 1960–61 and Vice President of the American Ceramic Society in 1966–67. Since 1961, he has been chairman of the National Academy of Sciences— National Research Council's Committee on Ceramic Chemistry.

ELECTRONIC CERAMICS

Edward C. Henry

7044043

FORTSMOUTH
POLYTECHNIC
LIBRARY
666

PREPARED UNDER THE SPONSORSHIP OF
THE MANUFACTURING CHEMISTS' ASSOCIATION

Garden City, New York

DOUBLEDAY & COMPANY, INC.

1969

ILLUSTRATION CREDITS

The courtesy of permission to use or to adapt photographs, drawings, and tables from the following sources is gratefully acknowledged: PLATES 1, 4, 5, Philips Laboratories Division, North American Philips Company; PLATES 10 and 11, Corning Glass Works; PLATE 2, Centralab Electronics Division, Globe Union, Inc.; PLATE 3, Indiana General Corporation; PLATE 6, Brookhaven National Laboratory; PLATE 7, Westinghouse Corporation; PLATE 8, General Electric Company; PLATE 9, TAM Division, National Lead Company; PLATE 12, Western Electric Company; PLATE 13, Ceramaseal, Inc.; PLATE 14, Honeywell, Inc.; *Figure 2*, E. Albers-Schoenberg, "Ferrites," *Journal of the American Ceramic Society* 41 (1958); *Figures 5* and *7*, G. Shirane, F. Jona, and R. Pepinsky, "Some Aspects of Ferroelectricity," Proc. IRE 43 (1955); *Figure 8*, Floyd Allen, "Transistorized DC-to-DC Converters Employing Piezoelectric Transformers," TR-1116, Harry Diamond Laboratories, U. S. Army Material Command, Washington, D.C. (1963); *Figures 9, 10*, and *13*, E. G. Graf, "Glossary of Electronic Ceramic Terms," M & T Chemicals, Inc.; *Figure 14*, W. W. Coffeen, "Dielectric Bodies in Metal Stannate-Barium Titanate Binary Systems," *Journal of the American Ceramic Society* 37 (1954); *Figure 15*, Corning Glass Works; *Figure 17, Ceramic Age* (February 1966); *Figures 18* and *19*, "Eectroluminescence, Theory and Practice," *Electronics World* (January 1965); *Figure 16*, D. P. Burks, "The Use of Ceramics in Hybrid Integrated Circuits," Sprague Electric Company (November 1966); Table 1, R. B. Sosman, "The Phases of Silica," *American Ceramic Society Bulletin* 43 (1964); Table 2, W. R. Beck, "Crystallographic Inversions of the Aluminum Orthophosphate Polymorphs," *American Ceramic Society Bulletin* 32 (1953); Table 5, A. C. Allen, "Ferrites Skyrocket Indiana General's Production," *Ceramic Industry Magazine* (1967); Table 6, G. Goodman, "Ferroelectric Properties of Lead Metaniobate," *Journal of the American Ceramic Society* 38 (1953); Tables 8 and 9, R. Roy, "Multiple Ion Substitutions in the Perovskite Lattice," *Journal of the American Ceramic Society* 37 (1954).

Library of Congress Catalog Card Number 69–15167
Copyright © 1969 by Edward C. Henry
All Rights Reserved
Printed in the United States of America
First Edition

FOREWORD

Electronic ceramics are new types of materials with properties so different from those normally associated with ceramics that many new concepts in this field need to be explained. This book is an effort to fill the gap in currently available information about these new substances; it explores the question of how such materials can be "tailored" for specific purposes.

The technical demands of industry are changing rapidly. In constant development are materials that feature greater reliability, uniformity, reproducibility, and efficiency within ever-increasing extremes of temperature, pressure, voltage, vibration, and mechanical stress. Electronic ceramics are performing with amazing results in areas bursting with growth such as electronics, supersonic aircraft, deep-submergence vessels, and space exploration.

There is almost no limit to what can be accomplished with ceramics. Many developments only await a ceramic engineer discovering the right combinations of materials, temperatures, and pressures. Soon, for example, television and radio sets may be using ceramic components that will last a lifetime. Present heating and air-conditioning systems—advanced as they are—could be outmoded in a few years. Engineers have produced silent cooling devices, made with ceramic components, that will cool a refrigerator to about sixty degrees below zero Fahrenheit without moving parts. Such a material will permit the development of smaller and quieter air conditioners, and when run backward, so to speak, these ceramic components can be used for heating.

Ceramics (singular) broadly refers to the manufacture of any product made essentially from nonmetallic minerals by firing at high temperatures. Ceramic products include a wide range of substances, from nuclear-fuel elements to construction materials; from piezoelectric ceramics to high-tension insulators; from missile nose cones to firebrick and other furnace-lining materials; and from synthetic crystals to exquisite porcelains. In this text, we are concerned primarily with ceramics that show useful electronic applications.

Grateful acknowledgment is hereby expressed to Dr. W. C. Fernelius, Chairman of the committee for the *Chemistry in Action* series, for suggesting that this book be written, and to Dr. W. E. Chace, Director of Education of the Manufacturing Chemists' Association, for his helpful comments.

CONTENTS

ELECTRONIC CERAMICS

Chapter I

THE AGE OF MATERIALS DEVELOPMENT

KEYS TO PROGRESS

In the past eighty years or so our lives have taken on a richness and complexity never known before. Human activity has been revolutionized by a vast number of new discoveries and devices such as electric lighting, the telephone, and the automobile. Today the parade continues at an accelerated pace: slipping firmly into our civilization are the miniature radio, stereo phonograph, color television, and the silent refrigeration unit which operates without moving parts. Typically, innovations like these begin as luxuries and quickly graduate to the status of necessities.

But behind almost every great new industrial technique or product lies the development of a material which made the innovation possible. To find evidence of this, one need only look back at Thomas Edison's invention of the incandescent light bulb.

In 1879, people lighted their buildings with candles or with kerosene and gas lamps. Edison had sought a practical way to use electricity for lighting for several years, and the idea of the incandescent bulb did not strike him all of a sudden. Indeed, the inventor spent more than forty thousand dollars on fruitless experiments, and ruled out thousands of materials, before he succeeded in building a lamp which kept a loop of carbonized cotton thread glowing in a vacuum for over forty hours. Thus electric lighting was born.

And when we refer to Edison as the father of the light bulb, we often forget that he was first the inventor of the incandescent carbon filament. This was the discovery that made the bulb possible, and although the carbon filament has been replaced by filaments of tungsten and other high-temperature metals, the principle still holds.

Immediately after he produced a successful light bulb, Edison designed a whole electrical system for it. He went on to organize a company to distribute light and power to New York City. On September 4, 1882, a master switch was thrown at the Pearl Street power station and a number of lamps throughout downtown Manhattan blazed with light. The age of commercial electricity had dawned. In fact, history has shown that not only the light bulb but the immense web of our modern electrical industry was triggered by the discovery of a satisfactory material for the incandescent filament.

Also in the 1870s, Alexander Graham Bell spent several years looking for a way to transmit speech by wire. He reached his goal on March 10, 1876, after he had worked out a method of using a carbon grain button. This he attached to the diaphragm of a mouthpiece and was able to convert spoken words into variations in the current of an electrical circuit. We recognize Bell as the inventor of the telephone, but we sometimes overlook the fact that he was also the inventor of the carbon granule microphone.

A key to the success of the internal combustion gasoline engine, power plant of the automobile, was the invention of the ceramic spark plug. This device permits a controlled spark to jump a gap within the cylinder of the engine and ignite a compressed mixture of gasoline vapor and air at exactly the right moment to drive the piston.

MATERIALS FOR MODERN MAN

In the more recent innovations, a deliberate search for the right kind of materials has been just as important as it was to the investigators of several decades ago. We see this dramatically in the electronics industry. The miniature radio, for example, became practical with the discovery that certain substances would do the work of a *vacuum tube.* In earlier efforts to make smaller radio sets, electrical engineers had progressively shrunk the vacuum tube from its original light-bulb size to a device as small as a peanut. But their truly remarkable achievements came when they realized that the functions of a vacuum tube could be performed by a tiny chip of specially purified and prepared silicon or germanium—in short, a *transistor.*

Transistors had important advantages in addition to their reduced size. They could operate at a low voltage such as that provided by several flashlight batteries. Moreover, transistors used so little current that the batteries would last for several months. The shirt-pocket radio thus became feasible, and later experiments led to the lightweight, completely portable television receiver.

Another example of materials development lies in the evolution of the modern phonograph from the primitive "talking machine" which Edison invented in 1877.

The original machine converted impressions in the surface of a cylinder or disc into vibrations of a diaphragm via the medium of a steel needle. It was a mechanical rather than an electrical process. Sound level could be controlled only by selecting the proper type of needle. A "soft" needle brought low volume, a hard needle gave louder music. Nothing could be done to raise the volume above that provided by the hardest needle. Meanwhile, the quality of the sound depended largely on the characteristics of the "morning glory" speaker which was used, or the properties of the sound chamber in the phonograph cabinet.

The electric phonograph became possible when it was found that a small crystal of an unusual material known as Rochelle salt would convert the vibrations of the needle into electrical signals which could be easily amplified. Still later, research showed that a small splinter of *electronic ceramic* materials, if mounted in a lightweight phonograph pickup arm, would generate from a single needle the separate sets of signals necessary to operate the speakers of a stereophonic phonograph. Thus we see how new materials have greatly improved both the volume and quality of recorded sound.

Color television did not become a practical reality until special *phosphor* materials had been developed. Bombarded with electrons, these would glow with the desired intensity of light and the required purity of color. We now have refrigerators and air conditioners without moving parts, that is, without motors and compressors. They provide cooling solely as a result of the passage of electric current, and this wonderfully helpful discovery came from the study and improvement of *thermoelectric materials*.

THE PUSH FOR NEW MATERIALS

Working in laboratories and industrial plants in many parts of the earth, scientists and engineers are systematically producing an enormous selection of new and improved materials. Many of these find their way into new devices for the home, for business and industry, for the military, and for space requirements. The impact of these innovations on our civilization eventually may be just as great as that of the electric light, telephone, and automobile.

Some of these new industrial materials are quite unlike anything we've worked with before. It is exciting to speculate what additional benefits may come of them; what new "things" they will bring.

The field of materials development is also very attractive professionally; it offers rewarding careers to interested men and women. This deliberate and systematic search for new compositions—their development in the framework of new technology—has become one of the vitally important professional activities of our age. Perhaps never before in history have so many people been involved in the study of materials.

The area is so broad that we can only skim over it here. One place where materials development has great urgency is in aircraft design. Planes capable of flying at supersonic speeds require special high-temperature materials of great strength and flexibility, yet light in weight. Occasionally, a new composition appears with no immediately recognizable usefulness, and the search for jobs for such a material is a challenging experience. The great majority of substances now under study are intended to meet an existing need or an anticipated demand, however.

VARIETIES OF INDUSTRIAL MATERIALS

Historians have named the stages of civilization in terms of the materials which men have used most effectively during certain periods. There was a Stone Age, for example, followed by a Bronze Age and an Iron Age. The modern Age of Steel is said to date from the middle of the nineteenth century, which saw the development of the converter and open-hearth processes. It seemed once that we would have an Age of Ceramics, in which the silicate materials such as concrete, bricks, glass, and the like would take over, but the plastics quickly moved up to share the spotlight. It now appears that the industrial materials are in such a vigorous state of evolution that no single class of materials can be said to predominate.

Today's industrial materials may be divided broadly into three categories:

(1) *Metals* such as iron, steel, copper, brass, tin, and silver.

(2) *Organics,* which typically contain carbon and hydrogen and burn or decompose at relatively low temperatures. They include the familiar synthetic plastics and acetate compositions known by such trade names as cellophane, nylon, rayon, Lucite, Plexiglas, Bakelite, and Formica.

(3) *Ceramic materials.* These are neither metallic nor organic but are composed largely of oxides and mixtures of oxides. Typical ceramic materials include bricks, dinnerware, and window glass.

We will show in a later chapter that ceramics are subdivided into a number of separate product areas, any of which may be attractive as a professional career. For the past twelve years, I have worked with *electronic ceramics.*

These are among the most recent of the "new materials," and the field is advancing very rapidly; it has a bright and challenging future.

Electronic ceramics are unusual in many ways. Some are based on substances that exist in nature, although not precisely in the form in which they are now used by industry. (Their degree of purity, for example, may not be the same.) Others are strictly new compositions—nature apparently never quite got around to making them at all.

Chapter II

CERAMICS:
THE HEAT MATERIALS

We will now focus on *ceramics* and consider both the differences and similarities between conventional ceramics and electronic ceramics. The word ceramics (singular noun) has so many specialized meanings in addition to its broad or generic meaning that it has come to be quite confusing. To avoid misunderstanding, it will be helpful to learn the various ways the term is used.

In the most general sense, ceramics (plural noun) include all materials which are chemically inorganic except metals and metal alloys. Ceramics, furthermore, are made by high-temperature processing, and they can generally be used at high temperatures. In this definition, high temperature means at least above a dull red heat, above 540° C, or 1000° F. Many ceramic reactions take place at temperatures considerably hotter than this.

The word *ceramic* may be used as a singular noun, but it is more often used as an adjective meaning inorganic and nonmetallic.

SOME FURTHER MEANINGS

Materials are usually divided chemically into "organic" and "inorganic." The organics typically contain both carbon and hydrogen and burn or decompose at relatively low temperatures, as stated in Chapter I. Sugar, gasoline, ether, aspirin, and the plastics are examples of organics.

The inorganics, on the other hand, are commonly but inaccurately broken down for convenience into the "metals" and "ceramics." Metals are pure metallic elements and chemical combinations of these elements with each other, such as iron, copper, brass, tin, silver, gold, bronze, etc.

The words "metal" and "metallic element" as used here can be very confusing to the layman. The confusion comes about in several ways: First, we use the words *metal* or *metallic* to describe both a state of matter and a type of chemical element. This is a logical consequence of the fact that so many of the chemical elements are metallic in nature when they are in the uncombined, or elemental, form. Secondly, we commonly use a single name to designate one of these elements both when it is metallic and when it has been combined with a nonmetallic element and has lost its metallic properties. For example, the chemical element sodium (Na) is a silver-white metal, but the sodium in sodium chloride (NaCl), common table salt, does not have metallic properties; sodium chloride is classed as a nonmetallic substance. The crux of the matter is that we must distinguish between the properties of the chemical elements in several distinctly different states. To avoid confusion, perhaps we should always use an additional word, speaking, for example, of *elemental* sodium and of sodium *ions*. On the other hand, the chemist commonly finds that the context is sufficient: when he refers to the sodium content of sodium chloride he is referring to sodium ions; when he speaks of the sodium content of sodium amalgam, an alloy of sodium and metallic mercury, he is speaking of sodium metal.

Consider now the chemical element iron (Fe). We are familiar with iron as the chief metallic ingredient of cast iron and steel. But iron can become ionized and react with oxygen, for example, and form ferrous oxide (FeO), ferric oxide (Fe_2O_3), and ferrosoferric oxide (Fe_3O_4 or $FeO \cdot Fe_2O_3$). In the ionized state the iron does not have metallic properties—it is no longer a metal. To express this situation in still another way (and this will be important to remember in connection with Chapter V), one can have a piece, that is, a bar, rod, or any desired shape, of $FeO \cdot Fe_2O_3$, containing approximately 24 weight percent ferrous ions, 48 percent ferric ions, and 28 percent oxygen (in other words, 72 percent iron and 28 percent oxygen), and yet correctly state that the material does not contain any metal as such.

The ceramics are chemical compounds of metallic elements with certain nonmetallic elements of the periodic table. Ceramics are predominantly oxides, but many carbides, nitrides, and borides are included; these are the products of reactions between metallic elements and oxygen, carbon, nitrogen, and boron.

The above description of ceramic compositions is only a rough approximation, because it leaves unanswered the question of where to put the inorganic, nonmetallic substances such as elemental sulphur, iodine, chlorine, and the like, plus many salts like sodium chloride (rock salt), and other chlorides, nitrates, sulfates, etc. These are generally not considered ceramic materials for the reason that they are not produced, and cannot be used, at high temperatures. To re-emphasize the key requirements for ceramic materials: They are not organic, they are not metals, and generally they are made or used at high temperatures.

CERAMIC PRODUCTS

Familiar ceramic products include such diverse things as bricks, dinnerware (china, earthenware, or pottery), porcelain, glass, portland cements, and clay roofing tile. *Refractories* are ceramic materials having very high melting temperatures and used in the linings of high-temperature furnaces, ladles for steel mills, and tanks for melting glass. Many refrigerators, washing machines and dryers, kitchen stoves and bathroom fixtures are made of metal, but have a ceramic coating or veneer of fired enamel that provides a hard, attractive, and easily cleaned surface. Other bathroom and kitchen fixtures are made of a china composition. Nonplastic floor and wall tile, art pottery, terra-cotta, and wall plasters are further examples of ceramic materials or products.

All of these ceramics fit the definition by being inorganic, nonmetallic, and either produced or used at high temperatures. Thus, we can understand how it happens that such apparently widely different products as clay flower pots, eyeglasses, false teeth, the lens of a huge astronomical telescope, the nose cone of a rocket (and, yes, the kitchen sink) can all be called typical ceramics. This is what we mean by saying that the word "ceramic" broadly describes a large *class* of materials, just as the word "metal" covers still another large group of materials.

Electronic ceramics are ceramic materials used in the field of electronics. They possess normal ceramic characteristics plus unusual and specific electrical properties. As a consequence, they behave in an electronic circuit in ways not possible for conventional ceramics. Electronic ceramics usually differ from conventional ceramics in chemical composition, which accounts for their unusual properties.

SOME IMPORTANT PROPERTIES OF CONVENTIONAL AND ELECTRONIC CERAMICS

A piece of ceramic may be quite porous—able to absorb a large amount of water—or, at the other extreme, it may be as nonabsorbent as a drinking glass. There are all gradations between. The main portion of a ceramic object is called the "body." The glossy coating, if there is one, is called the "glaze." Many ceramic bodies contain a considerable amount of glassy material and are largely nonabsorbent. These are said to be "vitreous" or "vitrified," from the Latin word for glass, *vitrum*. Commonly, the larger the amount of glass, the more translucent the body. This is particularly noticeable in fine china and porcelain. Still other types of ceramic ware, however, may consist of a porous body covered with an impervious glaze. In physical structure, such an article resembles a blotter covered with cellophane. So long as the glaze is unbroken, the body cannot absorb water. If the glaze becomes chipped or cracked, however, it can no longer protect the body, and water may penetrate.

Electronic ceramics differ from many conventional ceramics in at least one important respect: They generally do not consist of fine crystals suspended in or bonded by glass, as china does. Instead, they commonly contain no glass. Therefore, they are often referred to as *holocrystalline,* meaning entirely crystalline. Some entirely crystalline materials consist of only one large crystal, and are known as single-crystal materials. Most holocrystalline materials, however, are made up of many crystals and consequently are called *polycrystalline.* Many high-quality electronic ceramic materials contain so few voids that they cannot absorb water, and they may even be gas-tight. We should note that to be consistent with the definition, we cannot properly call such a material "vitrified," because in fact it may not contain any glass at all. In this case, the nonabsorbent material is described as a "dense" or "impervious" ceramic.

HOW CERAMICS ARE MADE

Conventional ceramics are manufactured by a number of well-developed methods and processes. The basic steps are (1) preparing the material for forming, (2) shaping the article, (3) drying, and (4) firing.

Centuries ago, in making the crudest ceramics such as a clay bowl or a handmade brick, these steps were relatively simple. The potter or brickmaker worked a clay with water until the mixture had the correct consistency for the forming operation. If he could not find a satisfactory single clay, he used a mixture of clay. He then shaped articles by hand or with the aid of a simple tool or mold and set them aside to dry thoroughly. Finally, he heated these objects in a fire, preferably in a furnace or kiln, so that the bricks or bowls became hard and rocklike on being cooled. Today, modern household and industrial ceramics must meet more stringent standards of appearance and quality. As a consequence, each step has become much more complex. This is where college-trained ceramic scientists and engineers enter the picture.

The producer of electronic ceramics, however, has a double problem on his hands. He must make sound, top-quality ceramics. But no matter how good these materials are as ceramics, they must also, and without fail, be capable of performing all of the electronic functions for which they are intended. In many instances, it is difficult to develop the best ceramic and the best electronic properties at the same time—what produces a good ceramic may give unsatisfactory electronic performance.

Whether the ceramics are produced in the laboratory or in a large manufacturing plant, two characteristics are sought in all ceramics, but increasingly so in electronic ceramics: uniformity and reproducibility. Uniformity means that the composition and the properties are the same from one part of an article to another, and from one article to another in a given "lot" (such as a group of pieces made at one time). Reproducibility means that subsequent lots of manufacture or subsequent shipments will have the same properties and performance as the first lot (which normally serves as the basis of comparison).

The raw materials for ceramics are usually in the form of fine powders. A large amount of clay (ideally $Al_2O_3 \cdot 2SiO_2 \cdot 2H_2O$) is used in making many conventional ceramics. Clay ordinarily is not used in making electronic ceramics because most of the compositions either do not require or cannot tolerate any of the alumina or silica found in clay.

The ingredients required are weighed out carefully and thoroughly blended and mixed, either wet or dry, to assure uniformity and reproducibility.

The mixture of powders sometimes is heated to a temperature between 600° and 1500° C, if high temperatures are needed to cause essential preliminary chemical reactions. Despite the heat, the materials do not necessarily melt. The reactions often take place between two or more solid chemicals, for it is not necessary that a liquid or gas be formed. To the eye, the reaction product may look much like the original mixture, but X-ray examination, which detects crystalline structure, commonly shows that a new (different) material has been formed.

Ceramics are traditionally and easily molded or otherwise formed in a direct way into the shape in which they are to be used (a brick, a plate, or, in the case of electronic ceramics, a rod or a disc, for example). But in a few instances in electronic ceramics, shapes are cut or drilled from larger sheets or blocks, much the way small, intricate wood shapes are cut from a larger piece of plywood. Such "indirect" shaping is not widespread and is used mostly for making special and experimental items. It would generally be too time-consuming and expensive to make production quantities of electronic ceramics by this method.

Traditional ceramics, containing clay, often are shaped from material that might broadly be said to be plastic. Electronic ceramics are usually fabricated from a nearly dry, powdered raw material; this is pressed into shape, and the fired product requires little or no machining to bring it to its final form.

Drying is an important step in producing electronic ceramics in only a few instances. Ordinarily the amount of moisture used in the prepared body is so little that drying is not the problem that it is in making claywares, where considerable water must be removed.

Firing, the operation of heating the shaped and dried article until it changes to a hard, rocklike structure, is usually the most critical step in the manufacture of ceramics. The individual particles of the powdered raw materials are "sintered" together. That is, the particles are heated to just short of complete melting, but to a temperature hot enough to form a coherent mass. In many instances, as in the case of china and porcelain, the particles of one of the raw materials melt first and form a liquid that covers the unmelted particles. On cooling, this liquid (commonly in the form of a glass) becomes the glue that cements the unmelted particles together.

The considerable energy required for sintering and melting comes from the high temperatures in the furnace.

In addition to sintering together, the grains may change in size during the firing. Large grains may grow still larger, at the expense of the smaller ones. This happens because it is easier for material to move away from the surfaces of the small grains and join the larger grains.

There is generally some relationship between the grain size and the electrical properties of an electronic ceramic material. Sometimes a fine grain is best; for other uses a coarse grain is best. The arrangement of grains, their sizes (whether all small, all large, or with various distributions of large and small), their shape, and their orientation (whether pointing randomly or all aligned in some common direction) and the sizes and distribution of voids, all make up a quality called *microstructure*. By control of the microstructure the ceramic engineer can do much to control the electrical properties of the ceramic.

If any of the ingredients of the body will melt at the firing temperature to be used, the composition is adjusted to limit the amount of liquid and thus control any potential loss of shape. The surface tension of any liquid, which wets and surrounds the unmelted particles, tends to pull the solid particles together. This action greatly aids the process of densification. In addition, the liquid flows into and fills many of the voids in the material. In most instances, this liquid becomes a glass when it is cooled. This is the procedure, then, by which vitrification is brought about during the firing of a ceramic.

The top temperature to which a ceramic is fired is called the *maturing temperature*. Ceramic materials intended for various electronic applications are fired to a rather wide range of temperatures. This is not surprising when we consider their wide variety of compositions. Generally, 1000° C (1832° F) might be considered a low temperature, while 1800° C (3272° F) would be considered very high. In addition to specifying the top temperature to be reached, the ceramic engineer also selects the firing schedule, that is, how fast the top temperature is reached, how long it is to be held, and how fast the material is to be allowed to cool. All of these influence the properties of the product. Heat is acting on the material all the time it is being fired. Consequently, for reproducible results, it is necessary to take into consideration the total "heat work" to which the material is exposed during its firing.

MEASUREMENT OF TEMPERATURE

Because temperature plays such an important role in ceramics, the measurement of temperature is also most important. The subject of temperature measurements is called *pyrometry,* from two Greek words, *pyro,* meaning fire or heat, and *metron,* measure.

How hot is 1000° C? How hot is 1500° C? If you have looked into an industrial furnace, seen a coal fire, watched a glass rod being heated in a Bunsen burner flame, or observed a wire being heated by electricity (as in a toaster), you probably noticed that the glowing material had a "color" which roughly gave you an impression of how hot it was. Here is a table of characteristic colors for various temperatures, which may help you judge the temperatures of hot objects.

	Approximate Temperature	
Color	*° C*	*° F*
Barely visible red	480	880
Dull red	600	1100
Cherry red	700	1300
Bright red	850	1570
Yellow	1000	1830
White	1115	2100

Since most electronic ceramics are matured between 1200° and 1450° C, they are fired at a dazzling white heat, as this table indicates. The producer of modern ceramic materials, however, does not rely on his eyes to tell him the temperature of the furnace or kiln. Instead, he uses one or more of several methods of determining temperature. The two methods most generally used in ceramics are *thermocouples* and *pyrometric cones.*

If two wires of unlike composition are joined at one end, by twisting or welding, and if that junction is heated, a small voltage is developed that is roughly proportional to the difference in temperature between the hot and the cold ends. Such a pair of wires is called a thermocouple. Copper and an alloy of copper and iron (constantan) are usually selected for thermocouples for low temperatures. Chromel and alumel are the names of the two commercial alloys (of nickel, with silicon, aluminum, and chromium) commonly used for intermediate temperatures (to about 1250° C). Platinum and a platinum-rhodium alloy are used in thermocouples to around 1600° C.

In the laboratory, one uses a millivoltmeter, and refers to a calibration table to determine the temperature equivalent to the thermocouple voltage read on the meter. In the industrial plant, the thermocouple is connected to an electronic device in which the scale of the millivoltmeter (or its equivalent) indicates the temperature directly in degrees or records it on a chart (indicating or recording pyrometers).

Other Pyrometers

For still higher temperatures, above the safe operating range of metallic thermocouples, a radiation pyrometer or an optical pyrometer may be used. In both instances, a device outside the furnace "looks" into the furnace chamber to determine the temperature. The radiation pyrometer measures the temperature by the amount of energy radiated from a peephole. With the optical pyrometer, the operator sights on a selected spot in the furnace through a telescope. He then adjusts the amount of current passing through the filament of a calibrated bulb, mounted in the telescope, until the color of the furnace precisely matches the color of the filament. Because of the previous calibration of the filament, the temperature of the furnace is quickly determined.

Pyrometric Cones

Since the 1880s, ceramists have been using small pyramids of oxide compositions, generally mixtures of clay and other minerals, to indicate temperature. These pyramids, made of carefully standardized compositions, are known as pyrometric cones. In Europe they are known as Seger cones, from the originator, H. A. Seger. In the United States, the first standard pyrometric cones were manufactured by Dr. Edward Orton, Jr., a professor at Ohio State University in the early 1900s. The organization he established, the Edward Orton, Jr. Ceramic Foundation, is still one of the largest producers of such cones.

Pyrometric cones soften at temperatures as low as 585° C (1090° F) and as high as 2015° C (3660° F). They are spaced to indicate temperatures an average of 25° C apart. The original series of cones was numbered from 1 (1125° C) to No. 42 (2015° C). Later, it was found necessary to add another series for lower temperatures, going from cone 01 (1110° C) down to 022 (585° C). The softening temperature or "end point" of a pyrometric cone is defined as the temperature at which the cone bends over so that the tip of the cone just touches the base in which it is set. The actual temperature depends on the rate at which the cone is heated, being lower when the cone is heated more slowly. In this respect cones behave like many conventional ceramic bodies. Consequently, cones are believed to be more informative than thermocouples, which only measure temperature. Pyrometric cones are said to indicate "heat work" rather than temperature as such.

The temperatures required for ceramic firing are obtained by burning coal, oil, or gas, or by using electricity. In firing electronic ceramics, gas and electricity almost exclusively are used. The gas burners may resemble large Bunsen burners. With natural gas and air, temperatures up to about 1700° C are reached. Using oxygen instead of air permits one to get temperatures of 2100° or higher. For commercial electrical firing, current commonly is passed through rods of silicon carbide. These rods will develop temperatures up to about 1500° C. Molybdenum wire, protected by hydrogen to prevent oxidation, may be employed to 1800° and above.

How does the ceramic engineer know if the products coming from his kilns are satisfactory? Generally, it is impossible to tell just by looking at them. The producer works toward a set of stated properties, called specifications. Sometimes these specifications are dictated by the person who is going to use the material in the manufacture of an electronic device. In other cases, the producer himself sets up the specifications for his customers.

Specifications differ, from one type of material to another, but we may consider some of the more widely specified properties at this point.

DENSITY

The density of a ceramic, its weight per unit of volume, is a clue to whether it has been properly fired. With many materials, both underfired and overfired ceramics may have less than the optimum density. For this reason, a minimum value is selected, below which the material is considered unsatisfactory. Although it is not always true, in general the manufacturer tries to make his electronic ceramic as dense as possible because such materials usually have the best properties.

Since the density of a material depends so greatly on its chemical composition, that is, on the density of the atoms of which it is composed, the measured density value does not tell us much about the quality of the material unless we have a basis of comparison. For example, a completely dense alumina ceramic (Al_2O_3) could have a density of 3.9, while an equally dense ceramic of lead metaniobate ($PbNb_2O_6$) would have a density of 6.4 grams per cubic centimeter. Consequently, it is more convenient and informative to describe the density of such ceramics in terms of "percent of theoretical." This method of reporting commonly is preferred because the user can tell immediately how close the density of his ceramic comes to the maximum theoretically attainable. The density figure itself does not convey this information until it is compared with the theoretical value.

ABSORPTION

The amount of water or other liquid such as carbon tetrachloride (CCl_4) that is absorbed when a piece of ceramic is immersed in it, or the depth of penetration of a dye solution in a given length of time, are further indications of the soundness or densification of a ceramic. For many uses, the ceramic must be impervious to liquids and must show no dye penetration.

STRENGTH

Ceramic units must be strong enough to handle while being assembled into electronic components and devices, and strong enough to withstand the stresses they will meet in service. Minimum specifications may be set, therefore, on crushing strength, on tensile strength, or on cross-breaking strength (called modulus of rupture), depending on the expected use.

ELECTRONIC PROPERTIES

The electrical properties to be measured and the electronic performance to be checked, in testing the quality of an electronic ceramic, depend on the use to which the ceramic is to be put. Therefore, we will discuss these measurements when considering specific uses.

It should be apparent by now that the problems of determining the quality of electronic ceramics fall into two classes: ceramic and electrical (or electronic). Tests of quality may be made by two separate groups of individuals. This comes about because an electronic ceramic is seldom used just as it was made. After it has been approved ceramically, a number of other things may have to be done to it before it can be tested and accepted for industrial electronic use.

The manufacture of electronic ceramics is in sharp contrast to the production of a set of fine china, for example, which is ready for sale as soon as it leaves the ceramic plant. With electronic ceramics, electrodes may be put on and leads may be added to permit connection into an electronic circuit. The ceramic may be fitted with a metallic, glass, or plastic covering, for protection against dirt, moisture, fungus, or shorting caused by contact with other components. Such covering is called packaging or encapsulation. A ferrite ceramic, for instance, is wrapped with wire and assembled into a transformer; the transformer, in turn, later is assembled into a television set.

Some electronics manufacturers make their own ceramics and then carry them through all the processing and assembling necessary for their ultimate use. On the other extreme, another ceramic manufacturer may make only ceramic materials and sell them to companies that convert them into electronic components. These companies, in turn, may sell finished components to still other companies such as the manufacturers of radio receivers or electronic computers.

In any event, if you are an average consumer, you will have little occasion to buy electronic ceramics as such. You frequently purchase electronic ceramics without realizing it, however, for they are often the key parts of various electronic devices and equipment. In the next chapter, we will look briefly at specific electronic ceramics and their uses.

Chapter III

PUTTING ELECTRONIC CERAMICS TO WORK

Since the end of World War II, electronics has become the fifth-largest manufacturing industry in America. Sales have doubled about every five years, and more than half of this remarkable growth has been due to the increasing demand for new electronic equipment. A large share of the cost of such equipment goes into electronic components, many of which are ceramic materials.

TYPES OF COMPONENTS

The components of an electronic circuit are divided into two major types: dynamic and static. Dynamic or active components are the keys to electronic control; they include the principal *semiconductors* such as the *transistor* and *rectifier* as well as vacuum or electron tubes.* The static or passive category covers a wide variety of devices including capacitors, resistors, transformers, tuners, filters, and speakers, many of which were adapted from the electrical industry. These devices play a more or less passive role in the electronic circuit.

Many essential electronic components today are formed from inorganic compounds synthesized by high-tempera-

---

* *Semiconductors* are materials that conduct electricity less readily than a conductive metal but more readily than an insulator. The electrical conductivity of a semiconductor is generally very sensitive to the voltage applied and is a reflection of the impurities present and certain structural characteristics. A *transistor* is basically a device made by attaching wires to a small wafer of semiconducting material in such a way that it performs a function similar to that of a vacuum tube. A *rectifier* converts alternating electrical current to direct current.

ture reactions that occur in the solid rather than in the liquid or gaseous states. The resulting materials or articles are generally dense, hard, and brittle. Other compositions may be made by glass-shaping techniques, with or without later devitrification (controlled crystallization).

Inasmuch as these materials are inorganic, shaped by ceramic procedures, and fired at high temperatures, they are known as ceramics, although in many instances they do not contain a trace of clay, flint, or feldspar—the conventional ceramic raw materials. Instead, they are composed of compounds of various oxides which have long been members of the ceramics family, such as aluminum oxide or alumina, Al_2O_3; barium oxide, BaO; calcium oxide, CaO; magnesium oxide or magnesia, MgO; iron oxide, Fe_2O_3; zinc oxide, ZnO; lead oxide, PbO; zirconium dioxide, ZrO_2; and titanium dioxide or titania, TiO_2; along with less-familiar oxides such as niobium pentoxide, Nb_2O_5, tantalum pentoxide, Ta_2O_5, and various rare-earth oxides.

Some electronic ceramics serve only as small parts of complex devices, but in other cases they may constitute almost the entire component.

CLASSES OF BEHAVIOR

Electronic ceramics are grouped roughly into classes depending on how they behave in a circuit, that is, whether they show chiefly *magnetic, capacitive, ferroelectric, insulative,* or *resistive* properties. We will briefly discuss each of these, plus a few others.

(a) Magnetic Ceramics

Magnetic ceramics, also called *ferrites,* belong to a family of industrially manufactured descendants of one of man's earliest known minerals—lodestone, or magnetite. This was the "magical" stone used in the earliest compasses. "Ferrite" comes from the Latin word for iron, and the chief ingredient of ferrite is iron oxide. Some ferrites serve, for example, as efficient cores in transformers essential to television sets, while others are permanent magnets under service conditions which make them superior to the magnetic metals. A television transformer with a ferrite core is shown in Plate 1.

(b) Capacitive Ceramics

Ceramic materials that do not conduct electricity and possess what is called a high *dielectric constant,* that is, a high ability to store electrical energy, are used between the conducting surfaces or electrodes of a variety of capacitors. (A capacitor accumulates and holds an electric charge; it consists of insulating plates between positively and negatively charged surfaces.)

The dielectric constant, its variation with temperature or with voltage, and the electrical losses of the ceramic are dependent on the type of material and on the processing (firing in particular) of the body. Barium titanate, $BaTiO_3$, to which other titanates and zirconates may have been added, is used most commonly in this class of ceramic material.

The capacitor is probably the most widely used of all the static components of electronic circuits. It is found, for example, in radio sets, television receivers, and hi-fi amplifiers.

(c) Ferroelectric Ceramics

As the temperature of some of the electronic ceramics is reduced—during cooling after firing, for example—the crystallographic structure of the material changes suddenly. This change involves a shift in the positions of some of the atoms of the crystal, resulting in the appearance of *dipoles.* Dipoles are positive-negative pairs: equal and opposite electric charges or magnetic poles separated by small distances. A material is said to be ferroelectric when such electric dipoles appear spontaneously.

The ferroelectric condition of barium titanate, $BaTiO_3$,

comes into being when its temperature drops below 120° C. Lead metaniobate, $PbNb_2O_6$, is a material with a high ferroelectric transition temperature, or *Curie temperature*. (Named for the French scientist, Pierre Curie; the Curie temperature marks the point at which there is a transition in a substance from one phase to another of markedly different electrical properties.) Lead metaniobate becomes spontaneously polarized on being cooled to less than 570° C. On the other hand, it is necessary to cool cadmium niobate, $Cd_2Nb_2O_7$, to about $-80°$ C to develop its ferroelectric condition. All of these factors must be taken into consideration when selecting a ferroelectric material for use over any given temperature range.

Ferroelectric materials are used, among other things, as *transducers,* which means that they convert electrical energy into mechanical energy, and in an opposite direction change mechanical energy into electrical energy. They are used, for instance, in generating ultrasonic waves such as those employed for ultrasonic machining; in vibration detectors and phonograph pickup units, and in underwater sound detection.

(d) Insulators

At high voltages, high temperatures, and high frequencies, electronic ceramics require unusual insulating capabilities if they are to block the flow of current. The problem is noteworthy at present in high-frequency or microwave equipment. Electrical losses in the ceramic used for this purpose are given off as heat and may cause difficulties. There is a need for insulators that remain effective at increasingly high temperatures and voltages.

Among the new ceramic insulators are spacers of alumina, Al_2O_3, in vacuum tubes, and vacuum-tight envelopes of special ceramics—improvements over electrical porcelain—which are being used in new ceramic receiving tubes and power tubes.

(e) Resistors

Some of the electronic ceramics have the ability to pass only certain limited amounts of electricity and thus may serve as resistors (devices with electrical resistance). These ceramics are able to control the amount of electrical resistance offered, its variation with temperature, and its variation with applied voltage. The degree of control is not the same from one composition to another, however. Tailoring of properties for a resistor is a matter of controlling the composition, the processing, the temperature to which the ceramic is fired, and the kind of atmosphere in which it is fired.

(f) Miscellaneous Materials

Another group of electronically active solids is closely allied with the electronic ceramics mentioned above. In this group are the sulphides, selenides, and tellurides of various metals, all of which have certain similarities to the oxides. (Note that oxygen, sulphur, selenium, and tellurium are grouped together in the periodic table of the elements and have similar chemical properties.) This class of miscellaneous materials can be prepared—like the oxides—by high-temperature solid-state reactions.

These "quasiceramics" appear destined for a busy future, as they can be used in *photoconductive, electroluminescent,* and *thermoelectric* devices. These include headlight dimmers, illumination panels, and articles which convert heat directly into electricity.

(g) Composite Materials

For the sake of completeness we will mention two other electronic materials—*cermets* and *seals*—that do not fit easily into the categories just discussed.

A cermet is a mixture of a ceramic and a metal. It is a hybrid, in other words, having some of the properties of both types of material. The two phases exist simultaneously and work together to give the composition its ultimate properties. Under the microscope, however, one may separately detect the oxide and metal constituents.

The assembly of many electronic devices calls for joining two unlike materials such as glass and metal, crystalline ceramic and metal, or glass and crystalline ceramic. These "seals" must be completely gas-tight as well as strong, in most cases. The most important problem involved here is that of designing the shape and selecting materials so that stresses from heating and cooling will not cause failure of the junction. Certain companies make it their chief business to produce and market such seals for electronic devices.

SALES OF SEMICONDUCTORS

The semiconductors such as transistors and rectifiers were put on the market only about fifteen years ago, and the sales of these materials have since risen on rocketlike trajectories. The whole field of electronics has been doubling in size every five years, as noted previously, while the demand for semiconductors is doubling and even tripling annually.

Transistor sales, for instance, zoomed from almost nothing in 1952 to thirty-seven million dollars in 1958 and should exceed three hundred million dollars in 1968.

Silicon and germanium rectifiers, which convert alternating current to direct current electronically, totaled about three million dollars in sales during 1956; they are expected to go well over one hundred and fifty million dollars in 1968. Total sales of all semiconductors is predicted to reach nearly five hundred million dollars in 1968 —a sevenfold gain over 1958.

SALES OF COMPONENTS

Total sales of both the dynamic and static forms of electronic components amount to between four billion and five billion dollars annually. Sharp increases in the manufacture of electronic equipment have resulted from expanding military and space demands and from the constantly growing use of electronics in industry.

Meanwhile, sales of electronic components are climbing much faster than the rate for whole pieces of electronic equipment. This is true because of the continuing need for replacement parts long after the original equipment—a television set, for example—is sold.

HOW ELECTRONIC CERAMICS ARE DIFFERENT

We have pointed out that electronic ceramics are typical ceramics in most respects. In the following ways, however, there are differences:

(a) Dimensions and Tolerances

Electronic ceramics are generally small in comparison with conventional ceramic products. Dimensional tolerances are extremely limited. In some cases, the allowable variation in a given dimension may be as low as 0.0015 inch, or 1.5 mils. It normally ranges, however, between five and ten thousandths of an inch (five and ten mils).

(b) Vitrification and Sintering

In firing conventional ceramics, the engineer will sometimes begin by forming a controlled amount of liquid. As a result of the liquid's high viscosity and surface tension and the fact that it usually becomes glasslike when cooled, he can expect to get an impervious, vitrified ceramic. (The word *vitrify* means to change into a glass or glassy substance by heat and fusion.)

But in firing electronic ceramics, the engineer generally cannot take advantage of any such effect. The amount of the liquid phase—if any—is very small. Therefore, the ceramist turns to *sintering,* a process by which a coherent, nonporous mass can be obtained by heating without melting. He must depend on this mechanism to produce ceramics that are impervious to water and usually also vacuum-tight.

(c) Crystalline Phases

The engineer who makes conventional ceramics is seldom concerned with the detailed identity of the crystalline phases in his ware, although he generally knows what they are. One exception lies in the manufacture of silica bricks, which are used in the production of glass and steel. In order to make the best silica brick, the ceramic engineer must produce a predetermined ratio of quartz, tridymite, and cristobalite. These are all minerals with different optical, electrical, and mechanical properties; they have the same chemical composition, however, silicon dioxide, SiO_2.

On the other hand, the engineer firing electronic ceramics usually must watch for a specific single crystal phase or solid solution. For example, barium titanate ceramics can be modified and processed so that they have, at room temperature, one of three separate types of crystal structures—tetragonal, cubic, and hexagonal. Each of these types has different properties. The engineer must therefore decide in advance which form he wishes to produce, and during processing he must avoid those conditions that would create other forms.

Rather small variations in a composition may cause large differences in the temperature at which certain crystallographic changes, or *crystallographic inversions,* occur. Thus, control of composition is one of the best ways to obtain a desired crystalline form having a stable temperature range.

(d) Polarization

For the best performance of ferroelectric materials, as mentioned previously, it is necessary to line up the dipoles in a common direction. This is done by putting electrodes on a ceramic piece and subjecting the material to a specific voltage at a given temperature for a certain length of time, depending on the characteristics of the substance being treated. This operation is called "polarization" or "poling." When the poling of barium titanate was first introduced in 1949, it was an entirely new concept in the field of ceramics.

(e) Purity

The performance of many types of electronic ceramics is very dependent on their purity. For example, vacancies of *anions* or *cations* (negatively or positively charged ions) caused by firing conditions or by lack of proper molecular ratios (stoichiometry) in the material can greatly change the properties.

Electronic ceramics are now being made of raw materials purer than any previously used for making any kind of ceramics. In some instances we do not know just how pure these raw materials ought to be, however, because we have not yet had the purer materials to work with. At the present time, there are few chemicals in sight having the same degree of purity as that required for silicon and germanium semiconductors, in which impurities are expressed in parts per billion.

(f) Structure-Sensitivity

Many of the electrical properties of electronic ceramics are dependent on the number, size, and arrangement of the tiny crystals, or crystallites, which form the ceramic. There is also a relationship between the electrical and mechanical properties of the material, but to a surprising degree these can be controlled separately. Therefore, the engineer must pay considerable attention to the structure, or texture, of his ceramic. The texture, for example, should frequently be examined with a microscope; in fact, the texture is commonly referred to as the microstructure.

(g) New Materials

The field of electronic ceramics seems now on the threshold of a technical eruption that could swamp the engineers who put these materials and devices to work. We are just beginning to appreciate the possibilities that lie in tailoring electronic ceramics for special, and frequently unusual, combinations of electrical and mechanical properties. In many instances, such combinations of properties seem incompatible with each other. That is, from what we know of these ceramics through training and experience, such properties do not normally seem to go together. The ceramic engineer must be alert for unique effects and their potential uses, however. Hardly any limit seems to exist in the number of modifications that can be developed—often to the astonishment of those working with ceramic materials.

The following list contains a few of the various properties that an engineer may be called on to build into his electronic ceramics, although not simultaneously:

1. Greater efficiency with lower electrical or mechanical losses.

2. Miniaturization.

3. Ability to withstand higher voltages.

4. Effective performance at very low or very high temperatures—or both.

5. Capacity for large changes in dielectric constant as a result of an increase in applied electrical field or a change in temperature.

6. Stability, that is, essentially no change in dielectric constant with variations in field, temperature, and frequency.

7. In electrical resistivity, the possession of a large or small change, or a positive or negative change, as the temperature is varied within set limits.

In the race for new materials and the quest for methods of tailoring existing materials, the ceramist turns for help to several companion fields of applied science. We will see in the next chapter how he draws on chemistry in particular.

Chapter IV

CERAMIC SCIENCE AND ENGINEERING

The potter of ancient Greece who turned out ceramic vases, jars, bowls, and urns would have been completely baffled by talk of electronic ceramics. Yet the college-trained ceramic engineer of the 1920s also was quite ignorant on this subject. Most of the "new" ceramic materials discussed in this book were unknown just four decades ago.

Exploding to life in the 1940s and 1950s, electronic ceramics touched off a revolution in the thinking of ceramic scientists and engineers. Up to that time ceramics had been prized chiefly for such qualities as rigidity, durability, resistance to heat and chemical attack, and for their sanitary features.

Then, suddenly, the ceramists learned that certain of these materials had stronger magnetic properties than iron and retained their magnetism at high temperatures; had a higher dielectric constant than any other known class of materials and could thus store large amounts of energy at high voltage; were able to convert an electrical signal directly into mechanical energy or vice versa, and could change an electric current into a temperature variation, or do the reverse.

CREATIVE STEPS

In the previous chapters I have emphasized the importance of controlling and tailoring the properties of electronic ceramics. First the ceramist takes various amounts of "dirts" and "rusts" (clays and oxides), mixes them thoroughly, and puts them into a furnace. He then exposes his mix to the effects of high temperature, sometimes a dull red heat but more frequently a dazzling white heat, for a specified time. Finally, he removes from the furnace a composition entirely different from the one he put there. But how does he know precisely what steps he should take? How much of his skill is based on tradition and inherited know-how, and how much on scientific principles?

CERAMIC EDUCATION

In every industry there is generally a *scientist* who does research, collects facts, and shows how these facts are related to each other and what the relationships mean. There is also an *engineer* who puts the scientific knowledge to work by designing and erecting structures, operating factories, producing articles, and the like. In ceramics—as in many other areas—we also find jobs with various in-between shadings, from the purely scientific to the strictly engineering. All of these jobs are about equally important.

The ceramic scientist or technologist is likely to be asked to do research—mostly of the basic kind—in an effort to learn more about the fundamental nature of the materials involved or to explain the reactions that take place while the materials are being made. Either a scientist or an engineer, or both, may be called on to develop new materials, new processes, and new devices.

An engineer is usually given the task of supervising the large-scale commercial production of a material or the industrial application of a process, however.

There are differences, although not drastic ones, in the educational courses recommended for ceramic scientists and ceramic engineers. Individuals in both professional areas must study certain basic subjects, but the points of view from which these subjects are taught often vary. Consequently, some ceramic engineers are engaged in research and development as well as in commercial production. Actually, before the first college curriculum in ceramics was established, a ceramist was considered neither a scientist nor an engineer but an artisan—a skilled worker.

DAYS OF THE ARTISAN

In ancient days the secrets of pottery-making were handed down from father to son and from master to apprentice. This was easy to do when no more than one or two raw materials were used and the body of the ware was relatively simple. The main problem was to develop skill in shaping the clay.

The Dutch tried to duplicate or even counterfeit the dinnerware they were importing from China; the result was delftware in the seventeenth century. True porcelain was invented by C. F. Boettger near Dresden, Germany, in 1709. Another type of ware, known first as bone porcelain and later as bone china, was being produced in England by 1750. Josiah Wedgwood (Charles Darwin's grandfather) was very successful with new ceramic types in the latter part of the eighteenth century.

At the beginning of the nineteenth century the compositions of these new kinds of pottery were no longer simple. They contained many ingredients, and among the substances used were two or more forms of clay, pulverized feldspar and other rocks, ground flint, and crushed, burned ox bones. There were now too many details to be remembered; it became customary for the potter to keep extensive notes, sometimes in his own personal form of shorthand, to assure secrecy.

These "black notebooks" did not contain incantations for the black arts, although this might have been suspected by the uninitiated. The books were filled, instead, with recipes for various bodies and glazes. Specific directions, based on previous successful results, told the potter how to correct his production difficulties.

As we look at these "rule-of-thumb" or empirical directions today, we find that many of them are still quite valid and can be justified on the basis of scientific principles. For example, the following admonition, "to prevent a body from cracking on cooling, decrease the amount of pottery flint, fire the body to a higher temperature, decrease the wall thickness, or cool more slowly," may seem confusing and somewhat like a shotgun approach. But these tips actually are ways by which one may successfully reduce the magnitude of the stresses which are set up in a whiteware body due to the fact that silica (pottery flint) undergoes a large and sudden volume change when heated or cooled through 573° C.

FIRST COLLEGE PROGRAM IN CERAMICS

Formal studies of ceramics were available in Europe, particularly in Germany, in the late 1800s, but they largely provided the type of training one finds in a trade school.

Dr. Edward Orton, Jr., son of the first president of what is now Ohio State University, saw that the ceramic manufacturers of that state would be helped if they could hire better-trained engineers to run their plants. Orton knew about the European programs, but he went a step farther and designed a course of study for university-level students. Thus the first college curriculum in Ceramic Engineering began at Ohio State in 1894. Some fourteen universities now have curricula approved by the Engineers' Council for Professional Development. Orton also set up a company for manufacturing pyrometric cones, a means of measuring temperature which we discussed in Chapter II.

Orton's first course of study was based on the assumption that the problems of ceramics could be controlled by chemistry. Therefore, great emphasis was placed on chemical subjects in the new ceramic engineering course.

TRENDS IN TECHNICAL APPROACH

Since 1894 ceramic education has changed in a systematic way that reflects the increased understanding of the subject. To bring about these changes, faculties have had to keep abreast of the important problems of their times. We can readily review the evolution of ceramic science and technology by noting briefly some of the problems that ceramists have considered most important over the intervening years.

Chemical Composition

As noted above, by the turn of the twentieth century, ceramists were well aware of the importance of chemical composition in their task of controlling quality and performance. When improvements were needed, purer raw materials were sought and deposits with proven uniformity were in great demand. Silica brick was among the first materials in which this approach was highly successful.

Later, probably in the 1920s, manufacturers turned to screening, magnetic separation, and more advanced types of purification as a means of upgrading their natural raw materials. Finally, to assure the necessary purity and uniformity, they began resorting to synthetic raw materials. These have been especially popular for electronic ceramics.

Degree of Sintering, or Density

When it became evident in the 1920s that good chemical composition was not the only thing necessary for good ceramic products, attention began focusing on the control of physical properties, namely porosity and density. In general, when a ceramic material is exposed to greater heat and fired a longer time, its density becomes greater and its porosity, if any, is lowered. Much effort was put into the development of precise, reliable tests for measuring these properties. Attempts also were made to discover if these physical properties had any connection with the performance of the material after it was put into service. In 1927, for example, we find A. V. Bleininger, one of the leading ceramists of his day, looking for a better way to determine the proper degree of sintering for a dinnerware body. By firing such bodies under different sets of conditions, he discovered, two samples of the same composition might have identical values of porosity and density and yet be decidedly different in other characteristics.

Phase Constitution

But then the ceramists learned that good chemical composition and controlled sintering were not enough to assure good, reproducible ceramic products. One needed to know, in addition, just what "phases" were present, that is, what specific minerals and glasses, and in what amounts, made up the fired body. This information was important because various combinations of phases in widely different amounts could be found in certain products, resulting in large differences in properties. Yet, if the phases had the same composition and only insignificant differences in density, this situation could not be detected by chemical analysis and physical tests alone.

The answer was provided by X-ray techniques for determining and identifying crystal structures. Introduced during the 1930s and 1940s, these techniques put ceramics on a more scientific footing. Now, for example, in addition to specifying acceptable limits of purity, porosity, and density, and without having to change these limits, the buyer of silica brick could obtain better quality by also specifying certain ranges of content of quartz, cristobalite, and tridymite (different crystal forms of silica, SiO_2) for his bricks. These three minerals would make up the *phase constitution* of his product.

Control of Microstructure

For best performance, it is still not enough to control only the chemical composition, density, and phase constitution of a ceramic material. We must also consider an even more exacting variable—*microstructure*. Coarse-grained bodies commonly have properties different from those of fine-grained materials which seem otherwise identical. For instance, samples of ultrapure barium titanate with almost exactly the same low porosity and high density, and the same crystal phases present, but with different crystallite sizes in the fired ceramic, are known to possess rather extreme differences in electrical properties. (See Plate 2.)

Four Variables

Today the ceramist attempts to control all four of the above-described variables: (1) chemical composition, (2) degree of sintering, (3) phase constitution, and (4) microstructure. He learns how to do this in college courses and from continued studies after graduation. The modern curriculum teaches not only the chemical composition and physical properties of ceramic raw materials, but how bodies are mixed, shaped, dried, and fired. The student acquires knowledge about fuels, how the required heat is produced, and how temperatures are measured. He is shown how the finished products are checked and tested, both to determine the degree of sintering and to be certain the desired properties have been attained.

Along the way he studies how natural and synthetic minerals make up the phase constitution of a ceramic and learns the chemical reactions by which such minerals are formed. He also discovers that many high-temperature reactions between oxides take place slowly, and that, in many instances, such reactions are not completed in the time allowed for the firing of a ceramic body.

In the manufacture of electronic ceramics, crystal chemistry and solid state physics are key sciences; I have chosen them to illustrate specifically how scientists and engineers work in this field.

THE ROLE OF CRYSTAL CHEMISTRY

Crystal chemistry in its broadest sense is the study of the internal structure of a solid and the relationships between this structure and the chemical and physical properties of the material. Crystal chemistry works in two directions: On the one hand it tries to interpret the properties of a substance in terms of its atomic structure, while on the other hand it attempts to assign to a structural feature a characteristic set of chemical and physical properties.

Ideally, crystal chemistry should make it possible for us to predict and synthesize chemical compounds having any desired combination of properties. There are four key aspects in crystal chemistry: (1) the three-dimensional geometrical arrangement of atoms in space, which is specific for any compound (in a crystalline material this is called the crystal structure); (2) the sizes of the atoms or ions that go into the structure; (3) coordination, or the ways by which atoms are clustered with and surrounded by their neighbors, and (4) the nature of the forces between the atoms, that is, the atomic bonds.

The relationships between crystal structures, bond types, and properties are frequently quite clear. For example, the principles of crystal chemistry have been used successfully to explain the flaky nature of mica, the hardness of abrasives, and the high melting point of refractories (for example, silica bricks). The flaky nature of mica is due to the fact that its atoms are arranged in such a way that the structure is reasonably strong in the length and breadth directions of the flakes but relatively much weaker in the direction in which the flake planes are held together. Abrasives, on the other hand, have very strong bonds between atoms; they are about the same in all directions. It takes a great deal of energy to pull these atoms apart. Hence, abrasive materials are so hard they can be used to cut metals. (Large quantities of abrasives go into the grinding and polishing of automotive parts.) Refractories also have very strong structures; much energy is required to disrupt their atoms, and as a result, many refractories make good abrasives. Examples of such materials are silicon carbide and alumina, which resist damage from both mechanical energy, as in the use of abrasives, and thermal energy, as with refractories.

Filling Space with Atoms

The regular arrangement of atoms in a compound is a matter of prime interest in crystallography. The sharp corners and smooth faces of a crystal generally reflect the layout of its atoms. Every crystalline compound has at least one specific way its atoms arrange themselves in space when the material crystallizes. Some compounds can crystallize in several arrrangements, depending on the conditions during crystallization.

When a compound can exist in two or more crystalline forms, it is said to have the property of *polymorphism* (many forms). Such a material is silicon dioxide, SiO_2, which is the most abundant material in the earth's crust. In the form of the mineral called low-quartz, silicon dioxide (silica) is the second most plentiful rock-forming mineral. Uncombined silica includes more than quartz, however, because it can exist in some twenty different forms. Each of these modifications, as seen by X rays, has its own characteristic structure, and each form also has different optical and electrical properties, different density, etc. (We have previously mentioned quartz, cristobalite, and tridymite as well-known crystal modifications of silica. Additional forms are listed in Table 1.)

If two or more minerals have the same structure, they are said to be *isomorphic*. A good example is seen in the similarity between silicon dioxide, SiO_2, and aluminum phosphate, $AlPO_4$. First, express SiO_2 as $SiSiO_4$. Then think of replacing one of the Si's with Al and the other with P. The valence of Si is 4+; Al is 3+ and P is 5+, but equal numbers of Al^{3+} and P^{5+} will average out to the same valence as Si^{4+}, so we may think of the cation (positive ion) valence as being preserved. The atomic radius of Al^{3+} is .51 Angstrom unit (AU); that of P^{5+} is .35 AU; thus the average radius, .43 AU, is close enough to that of Si^{4+} (.39 AU). (See page 41 for a discussion of Angstrom units.)

Due to similarities in atomic sizes and valences, $AlPO_4$ has forms that resemble quartz, cristobalite, and

TABLE 1
PHASES OF SILICA

CRYSTALLINE PHASES

Atmospheric Pressure	*High Pressure*
Quartz, low-	Keatite
Quartz, high-	
Tridymite S-I	Coesite
Tridymite S-II	
Tridymite S-III	Stishovite
Tridymite S-IV	
Tridymite S-V	
Tridymite S-VI	
Tridymite M-I	
Tridymite M-II	
Tridymite M-III	
Cristobalite, low-	
Cristobalite, high-	
Silica W	

AMORPHOUS PHASES

Atmospheric Pressure	*High Pressure*
Liquid silica	Compacted vitreous silica
Vitreous silica	Supra-piezo-vitreous silica
Silica M	

tridymite, three of the modifications of silica. The $AlPO_4$ form most like the quartz form of SiO_2 is the mineral berlinite. In Table 2, note the comparison between the properties of quartz and its $AlPO_4$ analogue. Quartz in many of its optical and mechanical properties thus resembles berlinite more than it does any of the numerous other polymorphic forms of silica, which we mentioned above.

In other words, quartz has more in common with berlinite, a material of similar crystal structure but different chemical composition, than it has with any of about sixteen silica minerals containing the same elements, in the same proportions, but having different structural ar-

TABLE 2
COMPARISON OF SiO_2 AND $AlPO_4$

	SiO_2 (*Quartz*)	$AlPO_4$ (*Berlinite*)
Cell Dimensions		
a	4.90 AU	4.93 AU
c	5.39 AU	2×5.47 AU
c/a	1.10	2×1.11
Density	2.65	2.56
Refractive Index*		
ε	1.553	1.530
ω	1.544	1.524
ε-ω	+0.009	+0.006

* Optical characteristics.

rangements of these elements. This phenomenon tends to illustrate a fundamental concept of crystal chemistry—that structure is often more important than chemical composition in determining the properties of minerals.

Atomic Sizes

When atoms arrange themselves in a crystalline structure, they behave somewhat like small rigid spheres with fixed diameters. We know this is not strictly true, but the analogy is convenient. Sizes of atoms were not known before 1920, when W. L. Bragg, an X-ray crystallographer, began working on the problem. Today we think we know rather well how the sizes range.

In crystal chemistry the most useful way to express atomic sizes is to report the radius in angstroms or angstrom units (Å or AU). This unit is one ten-thousandth of a micron, which, in turn, is one ten-thousandth of a centimeter. Thus, it takes 100 million angstrom units to equal one centimeter, or 254 million to equal an inch. The AU also is commonly used to express the wavelength of light. Yellow light, for example, has a wavelength of

5800 AU. By comparison, the radius of a silicon ion (Si^{4+}) is 0.39 AU.

Knowing the sizes of the atoms and their valence, we generally can predict what types of structure they will assume. We can make substitutions and replacements within structures known to have desired properties without forming a different structure. In order to get successful substitutions, it has been found that the radius of the incoming ions cannot differ from that of the original ion by more than about 15 percent. The radii of the ions (atoms that have gained or lost electrons) are very much dependent on the valences, and, to a much less degree, on the *coordinations* of the ions.

Coordination

Imagine you have four cannon balls and a golf ball. Place three of the cannon balls together on a flat surface so that they touch and form a triangle, leaving a nest in the center. Now put the golf ball in the nest and cover it with the fourth cannon ball. If the cannon balls are large enough, the golf ball is smaller than the nest or opening between the four; therefore, the cannon balls fit together the same as before. Now, if we substitute oxygen ions for cannon balls and a silicon ion for the golf ball, the silicon is small enough to be tucked into the space left where the four oxygens come together. In both cases the unit formed is in the shape of a pyramid, or tetrahedron. The golf ball has four cannon-ball neighbors, and the silicon has four oxygen neighbors. The silicon is said to have fourfold or *tetrahedral coordination,* and the structure is the well-known SiO_4^{4-} tetrahedron. If each of the oxygen ions at the corners were shared with another tetrahedron, they would form a network of tetrahedra with the over-all composition SiO_2.

The number of anions (negative ions) surrounding a cation (positive ion) is known as the *coordination number;* it is dependent on the respective ionic radii. A large cation may be surrounded by more anions than a small cation. If we think of fitting spheres (or atoms) together in various geometric arrangements, the following table will show the ranges of radius ratios (cation radius/anion radius) corresponding to the known coordination numbers.

TABLE 3

Coordination Number of the Cation	Radius Ratio, r cation / r anion
1	0–00
2	0–00
3	0.155–0.225
4	0.225–0.414
6	0.414–0.732
8	0.732–1
12	1–1

In electronic ceramics we are interested in coordination numbers for a practical reason. If a change in temperature causes a cation to become too small or too large for a given coordination, it will assume another coordination. This calls for a major change in structure. When the crystal structure of a material is changed, the properties are changed. So it is important that a change in structure be prevented within the temperature range in which the material is to be used. Ion-size combinations tending to give unstable coordination conditions must be avoided. Also, in making substitutions of one ion for another to modify the properties, we must be careful that the substitution does not lead to a ratio of radii calling for a different coordination than the desired one. This is particularly true in situations where the radius ratios as given in Table 3 are close to the upper or lower limits for a given coordination.

Bond Strengths

We have seen that ions have definite size relationships and that they arrange themselves in specific ways. But how are ions and atoms held together? Four major types of interatomic forces are generally recognized: *ionic, homopolar, metallic,* and *Van der Waal's.* Certain physical and structural properties are associated with each of these types. Ionic bonds are physically the simplest to visualize, and arise from the electrostatic attraction between oppositely charged ions (such as Na^+ and Cl^-). Homopolar bonds exist between like neighbors, as between the carbon atoms in diamond or in the formation of the chlorine molecule, Cl_2: they commonly involve the sharing of electrons. Metallic bonds are those associated with the coherency of metals. Van der Waal's bonds are the weakest of all and are typical of the binding forces in solid (frozen) inert gases at low temperatures. In electronic ceramics we are interested by far mostly in ionic bonding, but the other types sometimes are encountered as well.

Would crushed diamonds suspended in water or oil serve as a lubricant? Certainly not: Such a material would be abrasive and more suitable as a polishing paste. A suspension of powdered graphite in water or oil makes some well-known lubricants, however. And both diamonds and graphite have exactly the same chemical composition —carbon. The difference in properties can be explained by crystal chemistry, in terms of structure and atomic bonding. The crystal structure of the diamond is chunky and thick-set, while that of the graphite is platy or flake-like. Moreover, the carbon-carbon bonds in the diamond are a great deal stronger than those in the graphite.

Combining the large oxygen anions with small cations leads to some interesting volume relationships in ceramics. In a typical piece of soda-lime glass, for example, 92 percent of the solid volume is occupied by oxygen, 5 percent by sodium, 2 percent by calcium, and 1 percent by silicon.† Thus, although a large part of the glass volume is furnished by the oxygen (which, if uncombined, would be a gas at room temperature), note the dramatic effects of the bonding that results from the cations of sodium, calcium, and silicon. The oxygen tied into a glass

† A. G. Pincus, "Glass from the Atomic View," *Ceramic Age* 39 (1942), 38–41.

structure acts like anything but a gas, as anyone can attest who has bumped into a glass door.

The strongest bond in such a glass is the silicon-oxygen bond. This bond also contributes to the hardness and strength of silica (SiO_2), especially in quartz, a very hard mineral, which is used, for one thing, as an abrasive in sandpaper.

In working with electronic ceramics, we sometimes need to know the direction in which a material is polarized. (We mentioned polarized ceramics in Chapter III and will discuss them in more detail in Chapter VI.) It has been found that in barium titanate, $BaTiO_3$, one end of a polarized structure is attacked by acid more than the other. This is taken to indicate a difference in the strength of the Ti-O bonds in the opposing ends of the structure.

To explain briefly, the strength of the bond between two atoms depends on the distance between the centers of these atoms and on their respective valences. For a given type of structure the bond is stronger as the ions become smaller and their valences greater. For example, silicon carbide, SiC, a well-known abrasive, is composed of small, high-valent Si^{4+} and C^{4+}, with homopolar bonding. The general relationship plays an important role in the properties of model compounds, described below.

USE OF MODEL STRUCTURES

It is frequently convenient in crystal chemistry to make use of V. M. Goldschmidt's model concepts in studying specific structure types. A common kind of Goldschmidt model structure is one in which the radius of each ion in one structure is the same as that of each of the corresponding ions in a structure being compared; the charges of the ions in the two structures are different, however. Since the fluoride ion has a radius nearly identical to that of oxygen, some fluorides are models of certain oxides. For example, beryllium fluoride, BeF_2, is a model of silicon dioxide, SiO_2; because of its similar atomic sizes and radius ratios it has a similar structure (see Table 4).

Note that Si^{4+} has a radius of 0.39 AU, $Be^{2+} = 0.34$ AU; $0^{2-} = 1.32$ AU and $F^- = 1.33$ AU. Because the valences in BeF_2 are only half as large as those in SiO_2, however, the interatomic forces are much weaker. This is reflected in the fact that BeF_2 is softer than SiO_2 and has a lower melting point.

The above has been a survey of several aspects of crystal chemistry from a very broad and general point of view. The subject has a great many applications in electronic ceramics, such as in explaining certain observed relationships and in predicting the consequences of modifying a chemical composition. In fact, it is difficult to find a technical situation in electronic ceramics that does not touch somewhat on the area of crystal chemistry. We will discuss a number of examples of the crystal-chemistry approach in Chapter V (on ferrites) and in Chapter VI (on ferroelectrics.)

TABLE 4
COMPARISON OF SiO_2 WITH ITS MODEL, BeF_2

SiO_2:	Si^{4+}	0^{2-}
	0.39	1.32
BeF_2:	Be^{2+}	F^-
	0.34	1.33

(Ionic radii in angstrom units.)

SOLID-STATE SCIENCE

Solid-state science is concerned largely with the electronic structure of solids and with those physical and chemical properties which derive from electronic structure. It is a recognized specialty that is younger than crystal chemistry and in some ways an extension of it.

The phrase "solid-state physics" was coined only fifteen to twenty years ago. It deals with such things as the quantum theory of solids, ferroelectricity, luminescence, semiconductor physics, magnetism, magnetic resonance, and superconductivity. The field has developed so rapidly it now impinges on many other branches of science, both pure and applied. Typical solid-state devices are transistors and rectifiers made of silicon and germanium.

Solid-state electronics is applied solid-state physics and includes transistor technology, crystal growing, preparation of junctions, the study of semiconductors, applications of ferrites and ferroelectrics, thermoelectric properties and their applications, electroluminescent and related devices, photoconductors, photovoltaic cells, and solid-state batteries. Microminiaturization of electronic circuits is also largely a solid-state problem.

Crystal chemistry and solid-state physics are both included in modern ceramic curriculums, although the amount of these courses offered varies from one college to another. Graduate students preparing to do research and development work in electronic ceramics usually dig into these subjects quite deeply.

SUMMARY

The chief objective of a ceramic education is the preparation of men and women for professional activities in the ceramics industries. The titles of courses of study given by various colleges and universities are not necessarily the same, but the subject matter is usually planned in such a way as to give the student important background, basic information, and experience in the use of such knowledge.

On graduation, the ceramic scientist or technologist draws on his knowledge of inorganic and physical chemistry, crystallography, mineralogy, crystal chemistry, and solid-state physics to engage in research and development work. His major goal generally is to learn new things about the nature of ceramic raw materials, the effects of processing and high-temperature reactions, and the properties and performance of the resulting ceramic materials.

The modern ceramic technologist is very much involved in learning, in greater detail than in the past, the relationships between chemical composition, crystal structure, microstructure, and the degree of sintering of ceramic materials, along with their properties. He seeks to determine those factors that need to be controlled in manufacturing precisely tailored ceramics. His task is not complete until he has reported and interpreted his findings to the ceramic engineer in a useful way.

Meanwhile, the ceramic engineer is concerned primarily with the conception, development, production, testing, and use of ceramic materials. The job of the ceramic engineer includes activities normally associated with engineering, including economic considerations. Since he is a specialist in inorganic nonmetallic materials and in high-temperature operations, the ceramic engineer also deals with the availability and costs of ceramic raw materials, the design and operation of ceramic manufacturing facilities, and with problems of the inspection, testing, and sale of ceramic productions.

In short, the ceramic engineer is responsible for the design of ceramic compositions, products, equipment, and processes, and for the manufacture of these materials or products. He becomes involved in quality control, in recommending appropriate materials for specific applications, in engineering sales and services, and in administration and management.

Chapter V

FERRITES:

NONMETALLIC MAGNETS

The properties of magnetite or lodestone (Fe_3O_4) were known to early man, and because of its ability to attract pieces of metallic iron and hold them against the pull of gravity, lodestone was thought to have magic powers.

Today a wide variety of artificial magnetites and related minerals known as *ferrites* are being synthesized in this and other countries. Such ferrites are tailored to fit specific jobs; their properties are superior to those of the best natural magnetite, and they have a wide and useful range of applications.

The people who invent, develop, and supervise the manufacture of these magnetic materials include ceramic engineers and scientists, chemists, physicists, mineralogists, and metallurgists. In a sense, these individuals outdo nature, because they have learned how to predict the effects of deliberate changes in chemical composition and processing techniques on the performance of their man-made ferrites. This is rather amazing when we consider that the first usable modern ferrite was made in 1946.

It is important to remember that ferrites are oxidic materials, that is, they are compounds that contain oxygen, or mixtures of such compounds. They do not ordinarily contain any elements in a metallic form, yet they accomplish many of the tasks expected of magnetic metals. Their usefulness is a result of combination of two properties: high electrical resistivity and strong magnetic activity. This combination is not found in metal magnets.

The formula of the natural mineral magnetite (an iron oxide known as ferrosoferric oxide), on which most ferrites are based, is Fe_3O_4, but a better way to write it for our purposes is $FeO \cdot Fe_2O_3$. This latter formula helps explain that magnetite contains ferrous ions (Fe^{2+}) and ferric ions (Fe^{3+}) in the ratio 1:2. Manmade magnetites, i.e., commercial ferrites, also contain iron oxide, but in these materials other metallic ions also are present which control the magnetic properties. These added substances mostly have a valence of 2 and can replace varying amounts of the Fe^{2+} of magnetite. Among the elements used for this purpose are magnesium (Mg), copper (Cu), manganese (Mn), cobalt (Co), nickel (Ni), cadmium (Cd), and zinc (Zn). Because these added ions have so nearly the same size as the Fe^{2+} ion it is possible to make extensive substitutions and still retain the crystal structure typical of pure magnetite. Consequently, most ferrites have their constituent ions arranged in the geometry known as the *spinel structure,* which will be described later in this chapter.

Magnetic oxides generally are used in the form of tiny crystals tightly sintered together. Ferrites are typical ceramic materials in that they are hard, dense, and brittle. As pointed out in Chapter II, many conventional ceramic wares—household china, for example—contain large amounts of glassy phase in addition to crystal phases. Ferrites, however, are almost completely crystalline. For special uses, small ferrite units may be cut from larger pieces of essentially single-crystal material.

CLASSIFICATIONS AND USES OF FERRITES

One way to classify ferrites is by their magnetic response, or susceptibility. They range from "soft" (easily demagnetized) to "hard" or permanent types of magnets. Each variety has its own particular applications, some of which are shown in Table 5. Sales of all ferrites in the United States in 1968 are estimated at more than one hundred million dollars. Market studies indicate that this figure is growing at the rate of about 20 percent per year.

TABLE 5
FERRITE VARIETIES AND THEIR USES

Type	Industry Where Used	Composition
Soft	Entertainment electronics, radio communication, military electronics	Manganese, zinc, iron oxides Nickel, zinc, iron oxides Nickel, copper, zinc, iron oxides
Square-Loop	Computers	Manganese, magnesium, iron oxides Cobalt, iron oxides
Microwave	Communications, military electronics	Magnesium, manganese, iron oxides Aluminum, nickel, zinc, iron oxides
Hard	Permanent magnet motors	Barium, iron oxides Strontium, iron oxides Lead, iron oxides

(a) Soft Ferrites

Soft ferrites are used in television, radio, electronic ignition systems, high-frequency fluorescent lighting, touch-tone telephones, communication and radio-interference filters, high-frequency welding, submarine communications, and for many other purposes. For example, soft ferrites are extensively used in the cores of transformers in electronic circuits. They are particularly valuable in these devices because they have strong magnetic response and high internal resistance to an electric current. The "eddy currents" set up in metallic-iron transformer cores are responsible for much of the heating that occurs when such a transformer is driven hard, but these currents are not present in ferrite cores. (Eddy currents are induced when an alternating current is passed near a massive conductor such as that in the core of a conventional transformer.) As a result, ferrites make possible the small yet highly efficient transformers found in television sets, for example. (See Plate 1.) And the new wide-angle shallow television picture tubes were made possible as a consequence of the development of very powerful ferrites for the deflection yoke at the neck of the tube.

Soft ferrites also are put into radio antennae (they are often hidden in the handles of portable sets) and in the recording heads of tape recorders. Soft ferrites are made from compositions of manganese, zinc, and iron oxides (MnO-ZnO-Fe_2O_3), nickel, zinc, and iron oxides (NiO-ZnO-Fe_2O_3), and nickel, copper, zinc, and iron oxides (NiO-CuO-ZnO-Fe_2O_3).

(b) Rectangular or Square-Loop Ferrites

Certain ferrite materials have *magnetic hysteresis loops* with sharp corners. (Hysteresis loops are discussed on pages 57–59.) These are called rectangular-loop or square-loop ferrites and are illustrated in Figure 2(b). Such ferrites have two stable states of magnetization, that is, they can be switched sharply from being magnetized in one direction to being magnetized in the opposite direction. Square-loop ferrites may be produced from certain compositions of magnesium, manganese and iron oxides (MgO-MnO-Fe_2O_3).

Square-loop ferrites are used as storage units in magnetic memory systems of computers, in switching and automatic controls for processing and production equipment, and in other applications. Computer elements made of these ferrites generally are very small rings, or toroids, called memory cores. One type of toroid (the 20-mil size) weighs about six ten-thousandths of a gram. Consequently, there are roughly sixteen hundred such toroids in a gram, or nearly three-quarters of a million in a pound. A single computer can contain as many as eight million cores.

The sizes of these toroids have been shrinking over the years as the computer industry has stored more and more information per unit of memory space. The smallest toroids used in computers at present have an over-all diameter of fifteen thousandths of an inch, but 0.020-

inch and 0.030-inch cores probably account for more than half of the present market. The small sizes of these cores show up dramatically when compared with a man's finger, as in Plate 3. Such cores are shown mounted on a computer matrix frame in Plate 4. The market for memory cores has been doubling every three years, and today it exceeds six billion cores a year. This growth is expected to continue into the early 1970s, perhaps leveling off at between twelve and fifteen billion cores a year.

The fact that a single nonoperating core can spoil the performance of an entire section of memory makes it necessary to test each core before assembly or shipment. Because such a large number of ferrites can be made each day, plants are equipped with a number of completely automated test stations, each of which measures and sorts cores at the rate of about ten per second!

(c) Microwave Ferrites

The increasing use of microwave communications has brought a growing demand for ferrites in switching and control devices. Special materials, microwave ferrites, that have low electrical losses at microwave frequencies have been developed. (The microwave, a very short electromagnetic wave, has become enormously useful in voice, written, and television transmissions, not to mention several other types of communications.) Microwave ferrites are composed of magnesium-manganese-iron oxide ($MgO\text{-}MnO\text{-}Fe_2O_3$) and aluminum-nickel-zinc-iron oxide ($Al_2O_3\text{-}NiO\text{-}ZnO\text{-}Fe_2O_3$) types of composition.

(d) Permanent Magnet Ferrites

Ceramic magnets of the hard or permanent type contain a hexagonal crystal structure rather than the cubic or *spinel* structure, which is the most common ferrite arrangement. These hexagonal materials, known as magnetoplumbites, also are called ferrites, however. The barium and lead ferrites ($BaO\cdot6Fe_2O_3$ and $PbO\cdot6Fe_2O_3$)

are the best-known of this type. Hard or permanent-magnet ferrites are used in places where a strong magnetic pull is required—on a refrigerator door, for example. They also are used where a magnetic force is needed in the presence of a powerful magnetic field, as around a cyclotron, i.e., a particle accelerator. Here, ferrites are used by the ton. The 30-bev AGS accelerator at the Brookhaven National Laboratory has twelve accelerator stations, each about seven feet long filled with ferrite rings roughly fourteen inches in diameter and one inch thick. In all, this accelerator contains about seven tons of ferrite. Typical rings are illustrated in Plate 5; an accelerating station is pictured in Plate 6.

The automotive industry is rapidly replacing copper-wound DC motors with hard ferrite permanent-magnet motors. These are the small motors that operate windshield wipers, heater blowers, air conditioners, window lifts, seat adjusters, and convertible top raisers. On the average, each car had four such motors last year, and the number will increase. One manufacturer recently advertised a quality model with twelve ferrite motors per car. The change is being made to ferrite motors because they are less expensive, smaller, have better over-all performance, and do not contain a critical material—copper.

Permanent-magnet motors also are finding wider use in small appliances and portable electric tools, particularly the cordless type, because of the savings in cost and weight. It is reported that all of the electric toothbrushes produced last year, a fourth of the electric knives, and a fifth of all the electric shavers had permanent-magnet motors.

In the future we may see ceramic permanent magnets become the essential elements of a new concept in mass transit—the elevated magnetic roadway. Built into both cars and roadways, such ceramic magnets would "float" the vehicle by magnetic repulsion. The cars would be driven by a linear electric motor stretched out lengthwise along the top of the cars and along the underside of the roadway. An artist's drawing of this concept is seen in Plate 7.

MANUFACTURE OF FERRITES

Ferrites are made by typical ceramic procedures rather than by those used in metallurgy. Using mostly the oxides, carbonates, and hydroxides of the chemical elements to be incorporated into the product, ferrite batches are weighed out and thoroughly blended. Chemical raw materials for ferrites are purchased according to specifications of purity and grain size. Synthetic iron oxides of the type manufactured for paint pigments are usually preferred.

Sometimes added before the raw mix is shaped, dried, and fired are such materials as waxes, starches, and polyvinyl alcohol, or other binders, lubricants, and plasticizers. More often, however, the mixture is first calcined, that is, heated to a high temperature. This permits the ingredients to react with each other and create the desired ferrite material. The resulting calcine, with additions, is then crushed, milled, or otherwise processed into a condition suitable for shaping and firing.

Most ferrites are shaped by a process known as dry-pressing. The steps followed and the equipment used are about the same as those that go into such ceramic products as wall tile and floor tile. Other ferrite shapes —rods and tubing, for instance—are extruded through dies.

Among the variables that affect the properties of ferrites are the distribution of particle sizes, the pressure used in forming the article, and the shrinkage characteristics. But the most critical operation in obtaining the desired ceramic and magnetic properties is the firing. Not only must the firing temperature be closely controlled—ranging between 1250° C and 1450° C—but the oxygen content of the atmosphere in which the ferrite is fired also must be carefully regulated. There is a good technical reason for this. The ceramic engineer usually wants to reach and maintain some previously selected ratio of Fe^{2+} to Fe^{3+} in the finished ferrite, because this ratio strongly influences the magnetic performance of the ferrite.

PROPERTIES OF FERRITES

We can divide the properties of ferrites into two classes: ceramic and electrical. Ceramic properties such as density, strength, and shrinkage control chiefly concern the producer of the ceramic rather than the user. On the other hand, the user considers such properties as electrical resistance, Curie temperature, and the magnetic properties: initial permeability, maximum permeability, saturation flux density, and coercive force. High electrical resistivity inhibits the formation of eddy currents and is important in small transformers used at high voltages, as noted earlier.

We have seen that the Curie temperature is the temperature above which the material can no longer be magnetized. Ferrites have higher Curie temperatures than many magnetic metal alloys, but even with ferrites we are limited to about 640° C.

In both metals and ferrites, magnetic properties are described by their *hysteresis loops*. In Figure 1, we see that the hysteresis loop is formed by plotting H, the intensity in oersteds of the magnetic field of a test coil, against B, the magnetic induction or flux density of the substance (this also can be stated as the magnetic moment per unit volume) measured in gauss. The quotient is $B/H = \mu$, the permeability.

Again looking at Figure 1, and beginning at zero on the so-called *virgin curve* of the material, the magnetization curve starts with a fairly flat angle, the tangent (slope) of which represents the initial permeability, μ_0. With increasing field strength, B/H becomes larger and reaches its maximum value, μ_{max}, at a certain field strength. Saturation then takes place; the curve flattens out more and more and approaches its highest B value, the saturation flux density, B_s.

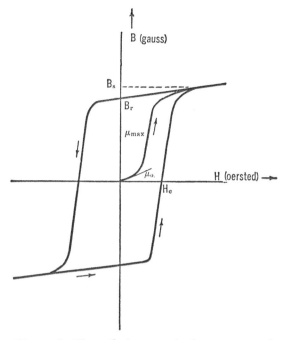

Figure 1. Theoretical magnetization curve and hysteresis loop.

When the applied field is reversed, the curve does not retrace itself because some magnetization is retained from the preceding treatment. The curve intersects the Y-axis at a higher point. From there it reaches saturation on the negative side and returns in a geometrically similar slope to the starting point.

The area inside this loop represents the hysteresis loss. The section on the Y-axis between zero and the intersection points is called the residual magnetization, B_r. Half the width of the loop, measured on the X-axis, is the coercive force, H_c.

A hysteresis loop such as the one described above is traced automatically on the face of a cathode ray tube when a sample of ferrite is tested in an electronic apparatus called a *magnetic hysteresigraph.* For research, development, and control purposes, photographs of these hysteresis curves commonly are made and entered in the records of the properties of a ferrite. Some typical hysteresis loops are shown in Figures 2a, 2b, and 2c.

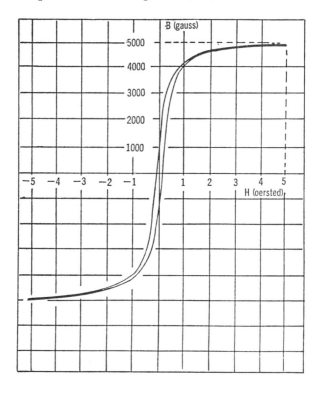

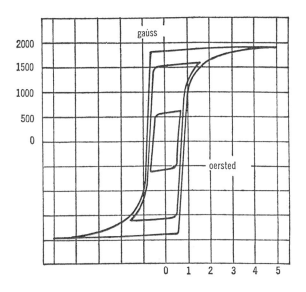

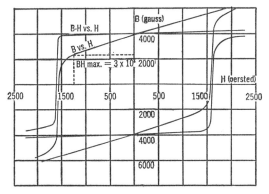

Figure 2(a). Hysteresis curve of a soft ferrite. *Figure 2(b).* Hysteresis curves of a square-loop ferrite. *Figure 2(c).* Hysteresis curve of a permanent magnet ferrite.

RARE EARTH GARNET CERAMICS

A material closely related to ferrite is yttrium-iron garnet (YIG), $3Y_2O_3 \cdot 5Fe_2O_3$. YIG is among the best-known of the rare-earth garnets. In single-crystal form or as polycrystalline ceramic materials, rare-earth iron garnets are used in microwave devices. Their main advantage is their very narrow *resonance absorption* line width, which results in low electrical losses and correspondingly high efficiency.

Yttrium-iron garnet is prepared by ball-milling (pulverizing in a ball mill) synthetic magnetite and yttria (yttrium oxide, Y_2O_3); by coprecipitating (precipitating together) the iron and yttrium as oxalates or carbonates; by milling the raw oxides, and by several other methods, followed by calcining at $1000°$ to $1300°$ C. The calcine is then crushed, shaped, and fired to $1340°$ to $1400°$ C. Development of the garnet phase is indicated by the color of the calcine, which changes from red to brown to green as the Fe_2O_3 becomes incorporated into the YIG.

These constituents must react completely to form the garnet, since any extraneous phases or inclusions will appear as voids to microwave energy. The garnet also should have high electrical resistivity, since conductivity would shield the interior from the microwave energy, reducing the desired performance.

MINERALOGY AND CRYSTALLOGRAPHY OF FERRITES

To the mineralogist, the word *spinel* denotes a specific mineral, magnesium aluminate, which can be expressed as $MgAl_2O_4$ or $MgO \cdot Al_2O_3$. To the crystallographer, on the other hand, the term is more closely associated with the structural arrangement of atoms found characteristically in the mineral spinel. The spinel structure is shared by a number of similar minerals and, as men-

1. Television horizontal sweep transformer of a 1950 type with a powdered iron core, and a present-day type with a ferrite core. Note the size reduction made possible through the use of ceramic ferrite cores.

2. Microstructure of high-purity barium titanate at four firing temperatures. These differences in microstructure lead to differences in physical and electrical properties.

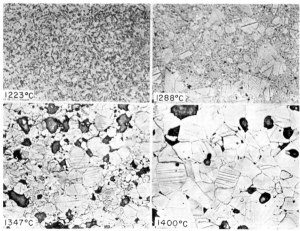

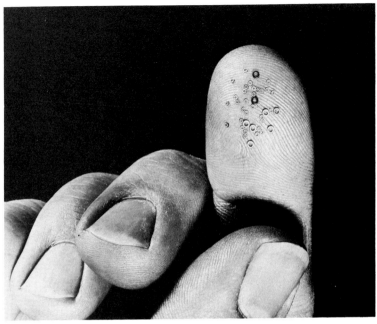

3. The small sizes of the various types of ceramic memory cores show up dramatically when compared with a man's finger.

4. A computer matrix frame containing 4096 ferrite cores.

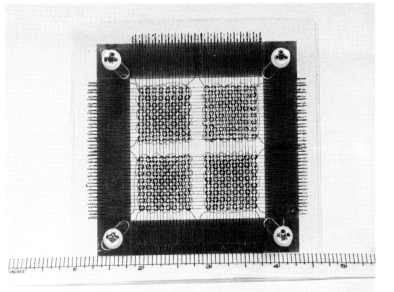

5. Ferrite rings for several proton accelerators. The largest ring, nearly twenty inches in outside diameter, is probably one of the biggest pieces of ferrite ever made and is of the type used in the Princeton-Pennsylvania accelerator. The intermediate-sized ring is of the type used in the Brookhaven accelerator, part of which is shown in Plate 6. The smallest ring was made for a European accelerator.

6. Internal ferrite structure for one of the twelve accelerating stations of the Brookhaven proton accelerator.

7. An artist's conception of a magnetic roadway. *Electric drive:* (1) Portion of linear motor attached to roadway and serving the same function as the stator of a conventional electric motor; (2) portion of linear motor attached to the car, functioning as a rotor. *Magnetic suspension:* (3) Ceramic (ferrite) permanent magnets attached to the car; (4) ferrite magnets attached to the roadway.

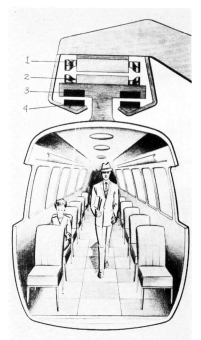

8. Small, rugged electronic tube with ceramic envelope, compared with conventional glass tubes.

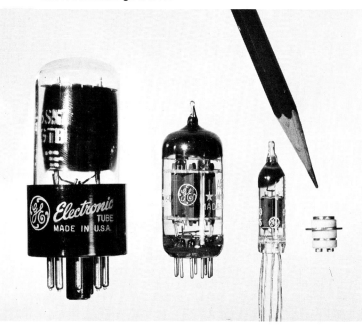

tioned earlier in this chapter, most ferrites have their constituent ions arranged in the spinel geometry.

Basically, a unit cell of the spinel structure consists of a cubic arrangement of thirty-two oxygen positions. Such an array has ninety-six potential cation sites. Sixty-four of these are tetrahedral (the small cation has four oxygen neighbors) and thirty-two are octahedral (the cation is surrounded by eight oxygens). In spinel, only twenty-four of these sites are used by cations—eight tetrahedral and sixteen octahedral. In "normal" spinels, two-valent ions occupy the tetrahedral sites and three-valent ions occupy the octahedral.

Magnetite and magnetic spinels have what is called the *inverse spinel* structure. In magnetite ($Fe_8^{2+}Fe_{16}^{3+}O_{32}$), eight of the sixteen Fe^{3+} cations fill the eight tetrahedral sites while the remaining eight Fe^{3+} and the eight Fe^{2+} occupy the sixteen octahedral sites.

In natural minerals, pure compounds rarely are found. The "species" of a natural spinel is designated by its predominant divalent and trivalent atoms, and the "variety" by its next most dominant constituent. Three major families of spinels are classified according to their trivalent atoms: (1) The mineral spinel and its associated minerals are composed of the various divalent atoms plus alumina, and their general composition may be expressed as $X^{2+}O \cdot Al_2O_3$; (2) the ferrospinels contain Fe_2O_3 ($X^{2+}O \cdot Fe_2O_3$); and (3) the chromites have Cr_2O_3, as in $X^{2+}O \cdot Cr_2O_3$.

Among the iron spinels or ferrospinels, for example, five species are recognized in classic mineralogy:

Name	Theoretical Composition	Divalent Cation
magnesioferrite	$MgO \cdot Fe_2O_3$	$(X^{2+} = Mg^{2+})$
magnetite	$FeO \cdot Fe_2O_3$	$(X^{2+} = Fe^{2+})$
franklinite	$ZnO \cdot Fe_2O_3$	$(X^{2+} = Zn^{2+})$
jacobsite	$MnO \cdot Fe_2O_3$	$(X^{2+} = Mn^{2+})$
trevorite	$NiO \cdot Fe_2O_3$	$(X^{2+} = Ni^{2+})$

In *nature*, franklinite has manganese atoms, and jacobsite contains magnesium. Thus, there is a remarkable similarity between the compositions of these natural minerals and their man-made commercial counterparts. The ferrite compositions were developed systematically in an effort to obtain the best possible magnetic properties and to tailor them to the requirements of the devices into which they were to be placed. No attempt was made to duplicate the natural compositions; there was no reason to do so.

MAGNETIC POLARITY AND
THE TAILORING OF FERRITES

Have you ever made a magnet? If not, perhaps you have seen an instructor at school wrap a few turns of wire around a bar of soft iron, pass a current through the wire, and thus create a magnet complete with north and south poles. In a manner of speaking, the atoms of iron already had magnetic force fields resulting from the orbital motion of their electrons around the atomic nuclei and the spinning motions of the electrons around their own axes. Passing the current through the wire caused a magnetic field to be set up in the bar, and the atoms of iron responded by aligning themselves in this field. If the current was then passed through the wire in an opposite direction, the induced magnetic field was established in a reverse direction and the iron atoms responded by orienting their magnetic fields in the new direction. A material such as iron with the characteristics just described is known as a *ferromagnetic* material.

The ability of a ferromagnetic material to retain its north-south poles is lost at a temperature known as the *Curie point* or *Curie temperature,* which we have mentioned before. In iron the Curie temperature is about 770° C. Above the Curie temperature such a material is only slightly magnetic and is then said to be *paramagnetic.*

Certain materials may be just as weakly magnetic at room temperature because their Curie point is below room temperature. Or it may be that they are not ferromagnetic and are always in the paramagnetic condition. A limited number of materials, however, actually reject a magnetic field; they are called *diamagnetic.*

Meanwhile, there are materials in which the atomic forces cause them to arrange themselves so that the magnetic fields of alternate atoms face in opposite directions. If these magnetic fields are equal they cancel each other out and the material has no net magnetization. Such a material is said to be *antiferromagnetic.* But if the material has a complex structure and the fields in the opposite directions are not equal, there is a residual or net magnetization in one direction. A material with these magnetic characteristics is called *ferrimagnetic.* These concepts are shown schematically in Figure 3.

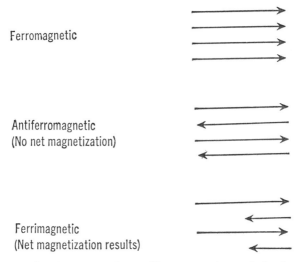

Ferromagnetic

Antiferromagnetic
(No net magnetization)

Ferrimagnetic
(Net magnetization results)

Figure 3. Ferromagnetic, antiferromagnetic, and ferrimagnetic arrangements of magnetization (schematic).

The ferrites—the center of our attention in this chapter —are ferrimagnetic. We have noted that ferrites crystallize with the "inverse spinel" structure, and that the Fe^{3+} ions are divided equally among the octahedral and tetrahedral sites, filling the latter entirely. We have good reason to believe (and our measurements agree very well with our predicted values) that the spins of the Fe^{3+} ions in these two sites are antiparallel to each other, thus canceling each other's contribution to the total magnetization. The resulting magnetic moment, therefore, is due entirely to the magnetic moment of the Fe^{2+} ions. Such a ferrimagnetic arrangement is illustrated in Figure 4.

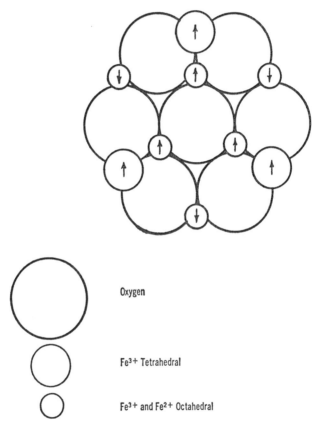

Figure 4. Spin directions in Fe_3O_4. Fe^{3+} ions in tetrahedral sites and in octahedral sites have antiparallel spins. The net magnetization is due to the Fe^{2+} ions in octahedral sites.

The above data gives us a valuable tool for tailoring ferrites. Here's an example of how it works:

Many of the ions used in making ferrites may occur in both the octahedral and tetrahedral sites. This is particularly true of Li^+, Mg^{2+}, Al^{3+}, Ti^{4+}, Mn^{2+}, and Fe^{3+}.

Zn^{2+} and Cd^{2+} tend to occur in tetrahedral sites, while Ni^{2+} and Cr^{3+} have a definite preference for octahedral sites. This behavior is not a whim on the part of the ions but is related to their electron-shell configurations.

The result is that if one needs to increase the net magnetization of a ferrimagnetic ferrite he can add a small number of Zn^{2+} ions; these will move toward and preempt octahedral sites, thus forcing some of the Fe^{3+} which normally would occupy these sites to go into tetrahedral spots.

Consequently, the number of Fe^{3+} ions in octahedral and tetrahedral sites is no longer equal; the contribution of Fe^{3+} in the two sites is no longer completely canceled. Instead, there is a net favorable field in the same direction as that of the Fe^{2+}. Thus the magnetic moment of the ferrite now includes a significant contribution from the Fe^{3+} in addition to that of the Fe^{2+}.

This illustration also points up the fact that the ceramic scientist working with ferrites needs to know such things as the electron chemistry of the atoms involved, the concepts of crystal chemistry, and the crystal structure of the spinels, all of which were probably covered to some extent in his college courses.

It should be pointed out that when a ferrite begins to cool, after having been fired to a high maturing temperature, the material is paramagnetic (has no magnetization). When it has cooled to the Curie temperature, the material spontaneously begins to polarize magnetically. Regions of material are formed in which the net magnetization of the ferrimagnetic "molecules" all point in a common direction. Adjacent to these regions are other, similar, areas in which the magnetization points in other common directions. Each area having a common magnetic direction is called a *domain*. The domains are large enough to be seen with the microscope.

If the ferrite is cooled through its Curie temperature under the influence of a sufficiently strong magnetic field, the directions of all the domains in the field can be switched to a single common direction. Domain switching helps explain the shapes of the hysteresis curves seen in Figure 2. For some applications, it is important to align the domains in some common direction.

MAGNETOSTRICTION

When a body is magnetized its dimensions are changed slightly, although usually by not more than a few parts per million. Such changes are referred to as *magnetostriction*. The property most commonly measured is the change in length in the direction parallel to the magnetization. Some materials such as the metallic metal permalloy have *positive* magnetostriction, that is, a bar magnetized in the long direction becomes longer when put in a magnetic field. Nickel ferrite, on the other hand, is an example of a material with *negative* magnetostriction.

This small-amplitude motion, repeated many times per second by making use of a high-frequency current, is an important effect. These controlled vibrations are useful in a variety of applications: ultrasonic cleaning; ultrasonic drilling; in detecting the depth of water (fathometer); in emulsifying oils, dispersing pigments, mixing paints, and in ultrasonic welding. A closely related effect called *electrostriction* is also valuable in the above applications. Electrostriction occurs in *ferroelectric* materials, which are discussed in Chapter VI.

SUMMARY

There are several types of magnetic, oxidic materials called ferrites. The most widely used ferrite is a man-made modification of the natural mineral magnetite, which in earlier times was known as lodestone. Commercial ferrites usually are many-crystaled, dense, hard, fine-grained, brittle ceramics which have been sintered (fired) at high temperatures.

Great advances have been made in synthetic ferrites during their brief history of a little more than twenty years. Skill in tailoring these magnetic oxides to specific needs has grown beyond original expectations. We can now improve their properties by numerous techniques, and we have put together some unique combinations of properties to meet new requirements. The scientist draws on many disciplines when he develops new ferrites. He knows that the effects of changes in composition will depend not only on which ions he adds, but also on the specific sites in which they will place themselves in the crystal structure.

The electrical performance of the synthetic crystalline material which results can also now be explained in terms of electronic and nuclear characteristics of the composition. Production engineers, as they fire a selected material into a ceramic having a desired microstructure, are learning to control the uniformity and quality of the ferrites more effectively.

Ferrites have been facetiously called "sintered rust with a college education," and this statement is practically true. Scientists, engineers, and technologists are doing a remarkable job of transforming iron oxide, or rust, and its related compounds into highly specialized electronic ceramics for the home, industry, and the military. In a sense, wizards of the laboratory and the manufacturing plant have attained the alchemist's goal of changing base substances into materials of great value.

Chapter VI

FERROELECTRICS:
THE ENERGY CONVERTERS

Ferroelectric ceramics have two very important capabilities: they convert electrical signals into mechanical motion such as sound, and in a reverse direction they change sound, motion, or pressure into electrical signals.

The best-known example of a ferroelectric ceramic is probably the phonograph pickup "crystal" which receives mechanical vibrations from a phonograph record via the needle and converts the vibrations into electrical impulses which are amplified and sent to a speaker.

Other uses of ferroelectric ceramics include ultrasonic cleaning, undersea warfare (underwater communication and submarine detection), and offshoots of the latter such as electronic depth sounders and "fish finders."

In the context of this chapter, ferroelectric ceramics are *transducers*. A transducer is a device capable of converting energy of one form to energy of another form; for example, electrical to mechanical or mechanical to electrical.

WHAT IS A FERROELECTRIC?

The term *ferroelectric* is used to describe both a type of behavior and the group of substances exhibiting that behavior. The prefix "ferro" comes from the Latin word for iron, but many of the best-known and most useful commercial ferroelectrics are ceramic materials that do not contain any iron.

To explain the properties of a ferroelectric, it should first be pointed out that most solids undergo a rearrangement of electrical charge when a voltage is placed across the material. All the positive charges effectively shift slightly in one direction and the negative charges in the other. In ordinary materials, the charges will "relax" back to their original places when the voltage is removed. Ferroelectrics make up a special group of materials which can maintain the charge separation without an applied voltage.*

This rearrangement of charges in ordinary solids has been compared by Dr. William Miller, City College of New York, with the activity that might occur in a roomful of both married couples and single men and women:

"The married couples are holding hands and will continue to do so. Suppose there are equal numbers of single men and women, and that the whole room is so crowded that people can hardly move. Consider what would happen if it were suddenly announced that one-ounce jars of Arpege were available free to the ladies, and could be obtained along one side of the room, and corresponding $1.00 cigars available for the men on the other side. The single men and women would all undergo a slight drift in opposite directions. The married couples would all tend to rotate so that the women would get closer to the Arpege. There would be a net shift of the centers of gravity of the two groups. Because of the slight drift, there would be no men along the end of the room next to the Arpege and no women at the other end. A very similar effect occurs in a solid when a voltage is applied across it. There is a slight shift of positive and negative charges in opposite directions with a rotation of paired charges (both plus and minus) called *dipoles*. Furthermore, a surface charge will appear at each end. The *dielectric constant* of a material is a number which indicates how much of a shift takes place."†

In a true ferroelectric, the dipole arrangement is a built-in property of the material, causing ferroelectricity

* *Glossary of Terms Frequently Used in Solid State Physics,* Dr. William Miller, Physics Department, City College of New York, July 1961, for a Seminar Sponsored by the American Institute of Physics and the National Association of Science Writers, Inc.
† *Ibid.*

to be established spontaneously. Also, in a ferroelectric, it must be possible to reverse the direction of the dipoles with a moderate externally applied electric field.

CRYSTALLOGRAPHIC REQUIREMENTS

Why do ferroelectrics occur in certain types of crystals? The answer begins with an understanding of *symmetry*. All crystalline materials possess one of thirty-two different classes of symmetry. This structural property, for example, can be easily recognized in a cube, which appears the same on all six faces. If rotated, a cube will look in many positions exactly as it did before. (Try this with a cube of sugar.)

Of the thirty-two crystallographic classes of symmetry, twenty are called *piezoelectric*—the prefix is from a Greek word meaning "to press." External stress of one kind or another on crystals in these classes will cause an electrical polarization. In ten of the twenty piezoelectrics the crystals are already polarized: They have at least one direction, or axis, along which the properties at one end are different from those at the other. These ten classes, a subgroup of the piezoelectrics, are said to be *pyroelectric*. (Here the prefix, also Greek, means "fire.") If the temperature of a pyroelectric is changed, the result is a change in the extent, but not in the direction, of polarization. Thus the term pyroelectricity: electricity released by heat.

The ferroelectrics, in turn, are a subclass of the pyroelectrics, and feature the spontaneous polarization characteristic of all pyroelectrics. But they have an additional property which is most important: The direction of their polarization can be reversed by an applied (external) electrical field. And still a third requirement of a ferroelectric is that the energy required to reverse the polarization must be smaller than an amount that would damage the crystal. The latter strength is known as the *dielectric strength* of the material.

From the above, it is clear that every ferroelectric is also a piezoelectric, but not every piezoelectric can be called a ferroelectric. In seeking new ferroelectric materials, the individual should look at various compositions that are known to crystallize in one of the ten pyroelectric classes of symmetry. The next test is to see if they have the additional properties, especially polarization reversal, that would make them ferroelectrics.

TWO KINDS OF FERROELECTRICS

It is convenient to speak of two classes of ferroelectrics: (1) the soft ferroelectrics, which are water-soluble, mechanically soft, and have low melting or decomposition temperatures, and (2) the hard or oxide ferroelectrics, which are formed at high temperatures, are mechanically hard, and are not water-soluble.

The soft ferroelectrics include Rochelle salt, sodium potassium tartrate tetrahydrate, $NaKC_4H_4O_6 \cdot 4H_2O$; KDP, potassium dihydrogen phosphate, KH_2PO_4; and GASH, guanidine aluminum sulfate hydrate, $CN_3H_6Al(SO_4)_2 \cdot 6H_2O$.

The hard (oxide) ferroelectrics have well-recognized structural characteristics. In Chapter V it was seen that an important group, probably the majority, of ferrites crystallize with an arrangement of atoms known as the *spinel* structure. Similarly, many ferroelectrics crystallize in the *perovskite* structure, which is named for the mineral perovskite, $CaTiO_3$, found in the Ural Mountains and at Zermatt, Switzerland, among other places. This structure includes barium titanate, $BaTiO_3$, and potassium niobate, $KNbO_3$. Other crystal types furnishing ferroelectrics are the *pyrochlore* structure (from Greek words for "fire" and "pale green"), of which cadmium niobate, $CdNb_2O_7$, is an example; *tungsten bronze,* $PbNb_2O_6$ and $PbTa_2O_6$, and *layer-type compounds,* $PbBi_2Nb_2O_9$. All of these structures have a common feature: the presence of cations, or positive ions, of small size and large charge, such as Ti^{4+}, Zr^{4+}, Nb^{5+}, and Ta^{5+}, in "cages" of oxygen octahedra (formed by eight faces).

PEROVSKITE STRUCTURE AND
ITS POLARIZATION

To illustrate spontaneous polarization, the perovskite structure of $BaTiO_3$ will serve as an example. Barium titanate, a synthetic mineral made by reacting barium carbonate and titanium dioxide, has the same structure as perovskite, since the Ba^{2+} ions of $BaTiO_3$ occupy the same positions as the Ca^{2+} ions of $CaTiO_3$.

The structure of $BaTiO_3$ is shown in Figure 5. We see here a cube with a Ba^{2+} ion at each of the eight corners. At the centers of the faces of the cube are six oxygens, which serve as the corners of an eight-faced octahedron. In the center of the octahedron is a titanium ion. Thus the structure in Figure 5 is an example of the "oxygen-octahedra" family of ferroelectrics.

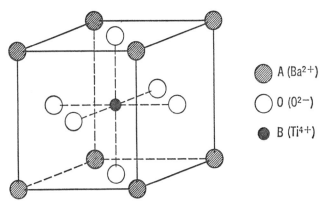

A (Ba^{2+})

O (O^{2-})

B (Ti^{4+})

Figure 5. Cubic perovskite-type structure ABO_3 (the structure of barium titanate, $BaTiO_3$).

When barium titanate is heated above 120° C (but below 1460° C) it has this cubic structure. In the illustration we see three crystallographic axes, indicated by dotted lines. Because the material is cubic, these axes are all of the same length. When barium titanate is cooled below 120° C (but above about 5° C), however, one of the axes becomes longer and the other two correspondingly slightly shorter. The Ti^{4+} ion moves off-center toward one of the two oxygens of the long axis, and this causes a polarization. In other words, one end of the long axis is more positive than the other, because the highly charged Ti^{4+} atom is closer to one end than to the other. As a matter of fact, nearly all of the ions shown in the illustration are displaced somewhat when the barium titanate changes from the cubic to the tetragonal symmetry. This has been discovered by neutron diffraction measurements. But for purposes of understanding polarization it is good enough to remember that the central Ti^{4+} ion is displaced considerably more than any of the Ba^{2+} or O^{2-} ions.

If left to chance, the Ti can move in any of six directions shown in Figure 5: up or down on the vertical axis, left or right on the crosswise axis, and in or out on the front-to-back axis. Or, to think of it another way, in every case where cubic unpolarized barium titanate is cooled to 120° C, the ion must first decide which of the three equal cubic axes will become the unique, or long axis, and then decide in which of the two possible directions it will move along that axis. Fortunately, we can make both of these decisions for the Ti ion, and thereby hangs the secret of the importance of ferroelectric ceramics.

In a single crystal of barium titanate, the dipoles in one area may point in one direction, while those in another portion may point in another direction, 90° or 180° away from the first. A region of material in which the dipoles are aligned in a common direction is called a *domain*. In Chapter V we saw that a region of magnetic material in which the magnetic moments point in a common direction is called a domain. Thus a single crystal of ferroelectric composition may contain several domains. If the crystal is heated above 120° it becomes cubic and loses its domains. Now, if a field is applied (about twenty volts per mil, or twenty thousand volts per inch) and the crystal is cooled through the phase transformation with the field still in place, the crystal will have all its dipoles aligned in the direction of the field. It then becomes a "single-domain" crystal. This procedure is called polarization, or, more commonly, *poling.* Polycrystalline, or ceramic, ferroelectrics can be poled similarly, as we will discuss in more detail later in this chapter.

COMPLEX DIPOLE ARRANGEMENTS

In a ferroelectric material the dipoles in a domain are aligned in a parallel manner. By definition, the direction of alignment can be reversed by an imposed electric field.

In some materials, such as sodium niobate and lead zirconate, the dipoles created by the displacement of the central cations relative to the oxygens are arranged so that alternate dipoles point in opposite directions. And because the adjacent dipoles thus cancel each other, there is no net or over-all polarization. A composition with this arrangement of dipoles is said to be *antiferroelectric.*

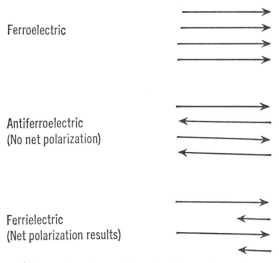

Figure 6. Ferroelectric, antiferroelectric, and ferrielectric arrangements of dipoles (schematic).

It is suspected that in certain other materials, solid solutions of one ferroelectric in another, the dipoles of one composition may arrange themselves antiparallel to those of the other composition. If the dipoles of the one composition are stronger than those of the other, cancellation will not be complete and there will be a net, or residual polarization in one direction. Such a material would be called *ferrielectric*.

Ferroelectric, antiferroelectric, and ferrielectric domains are illustrated in Figure 6.

SIMILARITY TO MAGNETIC CHARACTERISTICS

If the words ferroelectric, antiferroelectric, and ferrielectric seem familiar, it is because we recognized and studied similar terms in an earlier discussion of magnetic polarization (see Chapter V). Ferroelectric, antiferroelectric, and ferrielectric are counterparts of ferromagnetic, antiferromagnetic, and ferrimagnetic. There are further analogies: The temperature above which a ferroelectric is no longer polarized is called its *Curie point* because it resembles the Curie point of a ferromagnetic material. Ferroelectric substances above their Curie temperature are said to be *paraelectric;* you will recall that a ferromagnetic material above its Curie point is *paramagnetic.*

Ferroelectrics resemble magnetics in still another respect: They, too, have a characteristic *hysteresis curve,* which indicates a lagging or retardation of an effect during repeated applications of force. In the case of ferroelectrics, the hysteresis curve comes from plotting a different set of properties. In Figure 1, Chapter V, the hysteresis loop of ferromagnetics was obtained by plotting magnetic flux density vs. magnetic field. In a like manner, the ferroelectric materials show a hysteresis curve when polarization is plotted against applied electrical field.

The hysteresis loop of a ferroelectric is governed by the spontaneous polarization of the material, the existence of domains, and the ability to change polarization (and domain) directions under an externally applied field. Such a loop is illustrated in Figure 7. Here we assume a crystal containing an equal number of positive and negative domains, that is, domains antiparallel with respect to a selected crystallographic direction. Upon increasing the

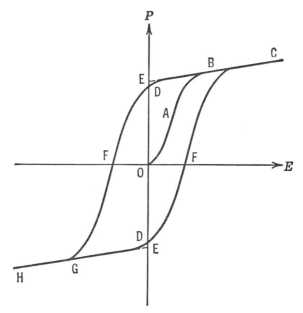

Figure 7. Ferroelectric hysteresis loop (schematic). OE = Spontaneous polarization P_s. OF = Coercive field strength E_c.

field (E) in the positive direction, the positive domains grow at the expense of the negative domains. The polarization (P) increases sharply (see OA, Figure 7) and reaches a saturation value (BC) when all of the domains are aligned in the direction of the field. The crystal now has a "single domain" structure. When the field is again reduced to zero, a few domains remain aligned. At zero field a definite value of polarization can be measured, and this is called the *remanent polarization,* P_r (OD). Now if we project the straight portion (BC) of the hysteresis curve back to the polarization axis, we have the value of the *spontaneous polarization*, P_s (OE). To cancel out the remanent polarization, it is necessary to apply an electric field in the opposite (negative) direction. The field required for this purpose is called the *coercive field*, E_c (OF). With further increase of field in the negative direction, uniform alignment of the dipoles again is reached, but this time in the direction opposite to the previous one (GH).

The ferroelectric hysteresis loop can be viewed directly on a cathode ray oscilloscope by means of a circuit first described by C. B. Sawyer and C. H. Tower, and therefore known as the Sawyer-Tower circuit. If the distances on the screen of the cathode ray tube have first been calibrated, the values of the key points on the loop can be read directly from the trace. Samples of unknown materials are given this test to see if they are ferroelectric, since only ferroelectric materials will yield this type of curve. It is also possible to determine the Curie point of a material by heating or cooling it and noting the temperature at which the hysteresis loop disappears.

The fact that ferroelectric materials can be poled in either of two directions, just as magnetic materials can be magnetized in opposite directions, means that ferroelectric materials could be used in electronic computers. To date, however, it has been more convenient, from the standpoint both of availability of materials and of circuitry, to put the greater emphasis in computer development on magnetic materials.

FERROELECTRIC CERAMICS

As we turn to a study of practical applications, a brief review may be helpful. Certainly the most important aspect of ferroelectrics, as pointed out several times in this chapter, is the fact that these materials contain randomly oriented dipoles which can be aligned in a common direction by an electrical force.

It has also been noted that a single ferroelectric crystal, whether single-domain or multi-domain, can be poled in a preferred direction, but only along one or more crystallographic paths. The number of possible directions depends on the crystal symmetry of the material, that is, on the number of axes along which the structure will permit poling to occur.

Some ferroelectrics can be poled in only one axis, others along two axes, and barium titanate, as we have seen, along three axes. And since we can pole in either of two directions along each axis, this means that a barium titanate crystal can be aligned in any one of six directions. Single crystals are expensive, however; they cannot be obtained conveniently in all compositions, and seldom are they large enough to be used for many purposes.

The answer is provided by ceramic ferroelectrics, which are produced by the conventional methods of mixing, forming, or shaping, and firing ceramic powders. This polycrystalline form of the oxide ferroelectrics can be turned out in nearly any desired size and shape of unit. In poling, metal electrodes are attached to selected areas of the unit, electrical contact is made to the electrodes, and a field is applied. During this step it is common practice to immerse the ceramic material in a silicone or other insulating oil to prevent arcing, since a rather high voltage is used. Likewise, to speed up poling and produce a more complete alignment of all the dipoles, a ceramic is frequently heated before it is poled. Barium titanate requires a lower voltage than many other ferroelectric ceramics, but the field it needs is still considerable. One effective way of poling barium titanate is to heat it to a temperature above its Curie point, 130° C for example, apply a field of ten to thirty volts per mil (or five thousand volts to fifteen thousand volts for a piece one-half inch thick), and keep this voltage effective until the material has cooled to 80° C or lower. Depending on the size of the pieces being poled and the amount of oil surrounding the piece, the procedure might require from ten minutes to an hour.

Ferroelectric ceramics are made from a number of

substances: barium titanate, sodium-potassium niobate, the lead zirconate-titanates, and lead metaniobate. All these have varying characteristics which help determine which material is to be selected for a given job.

FERROELECTRIC BEHAVIOR OF BARIUM TITANATE

Barium titanate has a complex crystallographic behavior. If cooled from a melt of 100 percent $BaTiO_3$ it crystallizes, or becomes a solid, at 1618° C. It then has hexagonal crystallographic symmetry. On being cooled to 1460° C, this form converts slowly to the cubic structure seen in Figure 5. Cubic $BaTiO_3$ is stable to 120°, when the tetragonal and ferroelectric state appears. Barium titanate has two other phase changes, however, and both go from one ferroelectric form of symmetry to another. These are found at about 5° C and at −80° C.

Since the ferroelectric efficiency of a material is low as the material passes through one of these phase transitions, it is necessary to shift the transition point away from the temperature range in which the material is to be used. Transformation points and Curie temperatures can be shifted, in all the materials we have studied, by making changes in the chemical composition. In the case of $BaTiO_3$, for example, an annoying transition at around 5° C (41° F) is shifted to well below room temperature by the introduction of about 5 percent calcium titanate, $CaTiO_3$, when making up the ceramic.

USES OF FERROELECTRIC CERAMICS

(a) Ultrasonic Cleaning

In the early development of ferroelectric ceramics, it was found that ferroelectric devices could be used commercially for ultrasonic cleaning of various objects and materials, for example, surgical instruments in a hospital, a pair of spectacles in an optician's office, or a plate of metal that is to be processed. The material to be cleaned is first immersed in a liquid bath. Then a ferroelectric ceramic transducer, also in the bath, is vibrated at about thirty kilocycles per second by a controlled power source. The vibrations reach a frequency higher than sound (hence the name ultrasonic) and result in a very effective and thorough removal of dirt.

(b) Phonograph Pickup Units

A small splinter of ferroelectric ceramic, commonly a lead zirconate-lead titanate composition, converts the vibrations picked up by a needle set in the grooves of a rotating phonograph record from mechanical to electrical. In a stereo recording, two separate signals are generated, one for each stereo channel, as the needle simultaneously picks up mechanical impulses from two sides of the groove. Obviously the transducers must be very small in order to restrict the weight and pressure of the needle as it touches the record.

(c) Communication Filters

Tiny wafers of ferroelectric ceramics are used as "band-pass" filters in communication equipment. At the resonant frequency of such ferroelectric materials, their electrical impedance (apparent resistance) is very low. And by tuning small reeds of a ferroelectric-transducer substance to respond to specific frequencies, it is possible to adjust communication circuits to pass, or receive, these frequencies and reject all others. Such filters are quite important in cases where many channels of communication are to be carried in a narrow range of frequencies. They help separate one message from another. The use of these "electromechanical" filters would increase if ceramic ferroelectric materials with extremely stable resonant frequencies were developed, that is, with changes of only a few parts per million during temperature fluctuations.

(d) Gasoline Engine Ignitors

One new device contains a transducer of ferroelectric ceramic which generates a high electrical potential when squeezed. This device can be installed in a gasoline engine to provide a spark like a spark plug. Timing for the spark is controlled by pressure from a cam attachment. The invention permits a very simple and lightweight ignition for small engines such as lawn mowers, snow blowers, and the like. We may eventually see this principle used in automobile engine ignition systems.

(e) High-Voltage Step-Up Transformer

A dramatic demonstration of the capabilities of ferroelectric ceramics is found in a transformer which steps up the output of a twenty-eight-volt battery to two thousand volts or higher and yet is free of wire coils in the primary and secondary circuit areas. This transformer does not operate on the principle of induced magnetic fields as do more familiar transformers. Thus it can be used to measure magnetic fields without disturbing them; and it can perform in a magnetic environment that might make a conventional transformer inoperative.

In effect the new transformer is a transistorized dc-to-dc converter, using a bar of ferroelectric ceramic such as barium titanate, in which one end has electrodes

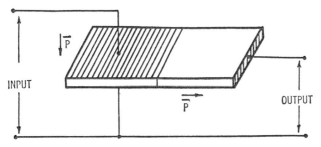

Figure 8. Ceramic high-voltage transformer (after Allen).

on the faces and is poled in thickness (see Figure 8). This is the driver, or primary end. The other end of the bar is poled in the length direction, has an electrode on the very end, and serves as the secondary. A typical transformer about 3 inches long, ½ inch wide, and $\frac{1}{10}$ inch thick, fed with a 28-volt signal pulsed at the longitudinal mechanical resonant frequency of the bar, can generate up to 2200 volts dc at 20 microamperes. The output voltage is controlled by varying the input voltage. For example, one report showed that 10 volts input gave an output of 400 volts, while a 30-volt drive yielded 2400 volts output. The usefulness of this transformer is clearly evident from its small size, its lack of need for wire coils, and its method of operation on an electromechanical rather than a magnetic basis.

(f) Sonar

Sound Navigation Ranging (sonar) is used beneath water much like radar in air. The sonar operator employs sound waves instead of radar's microwave radio impulses to scan the waters around his installation, usually a ship, and listens for the return of echoes.

To send out sound waves, he may use large transducers of barium titanate or some other ferroelectric ceramic. Such a device is called a sonar projector, and its material is chosen for its ability to handle high-voltage signals without shorting or otherwise failing. Certain substances have been developed especially for this heavy electrical-to-mechanical operation.

Echoes, on the other hand, are detected by hydrophones. These devices generally use a different type of ferroelectric ceramic, one that is extremely sensitive and can change a weak echo into a sizable electrical signal. This material is somewhat like a phonograph pickup material and was developed particularly for the mechanical-to-electrical step.

Sonar equipment has been put to work finding the depth of water, locating schools of fish, and, in undersea warfare, for detecting the presence of submarines.

(g) Sonic Delay Lines

Ferroelectric ceramic transducers can be used in making an electronic device known as a sonic delay line. In its simplest form a delay line consists of a bar or rod of a sound-transmitting medium. This can be glass, quartz, or metal, for example, with a transducer attached at each end. An electrical signal that is to be delayed is fed to the first transducer, which converts the signal into a sonic impulse. This sound wave travels along the sound-transmitting material at a speed much slower than electrons pass through a wire. At the far end of the delay line, the sonic impulse enters the second transducer, where it is transformed back into an electrical signal which now proceeds to its destination. The longer the path of the sonic impulse, the greater the length of time the signal is delayed. Delay lines are used extensively in military electronic gear and in color television sets.

CRYSTAL CHEMISTRY AND THE OXIDE FERROELECTRICS

Now for a look at several examples of how crystal chemistry is employed as a valuable tool in the design, development, and production of ferroelectrics.

Ferroelectricity Prefers Certain Structures

About a dozen years ago, it was noted that the oxidic ferroelectrics are characterized by small, highly charged cations in oxygen "cages." All materials with this feature are not necessarily ferroelectric, it was found, but within certain size-ranges of ions in these structures, ferroelectricity is likely to occur, and beyond these ranges ferroelectricity does not exist. In reporting such relationships, investigators have resorted to a sort of code to simplify their discussions. This is the "ABO_3 convention" in which A designates a large low-valence cation and B refers to a small highly charged cation. These requirements can be met with several combinations of valence, as shown by Table 6. Here it may be seen that tungstic

TABLE 6
CHEMICAL FORMULA RELATIONSHIPS OF ABO_3 AND $A(BO_3)_2$ COMPOUNDS

Formula Type	Valence Arrangement	Examples
ABO_3	A^{2+} $(B^{4+}O^{2-}_3)$	$BaTiO_3$, $PbTiO_3$
ABO_3	A^+ $(B^{5+}O^{2-}_3)$	$KNbO_3$, $KTaO_3$
BO_3	$(B^{6+}O^{2-}_3)$	WO_3
$A(BO_3)_2$	A^{2+} $(B^{5+}O^{2-}_3)_2$	$Pb(NbO_3)_2$

oxide, WO_3, is simply an ABO_3 compound with the A ions missing. The A ions are not needed, because the W^{6+} ions furnish the necessary charge balance.

Simple Substitutions

We will consider next an example of what happens when changes are made in the A-ion size when all else is kept the same. Let's assume we're interested only in making a ferroelectric with $A^{2+}B^{4+}O_3$. What ions can we use? In Table 7, the arrangement involves a series of A^{2+} titanates: $MgTiO_3$, $CaTiO_3$, $SrTiO_3$, and $BaTiO_3$. Strontium titanate, with A ions smaller than those of barium titanate, has a Curie temperature very near absolute zero. Mixtures of barium and strontium titanate form a complete solid solution series; the result is a barium-strontium titanate rather than barium titanate *plus* strontium titanate. The Curie temperature of such a solid solution is so directly related to the relative amounts of Ba and Sr that we can predict quite closely what the Curie temperature will be if we know only the *average* size of the A ion (it will obviously lie somewhere between 1.12 and 1.13 AU (angstrom units—see Chapter IV). A^{2+} ions smaller than 1.00 A, it is said, do not form ferroelectric perovskites; therefore, $CaTiO_3$ is not a ferroelectric. The A ion of $MgTiO_3$ is so small

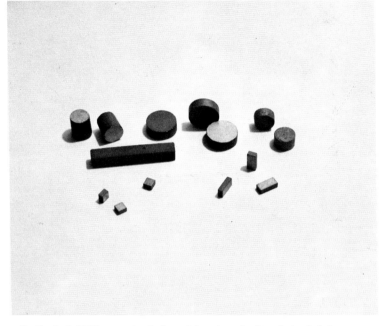

9. Typical PTC ceramics before (above) and after (below) being assembled into thermistors.

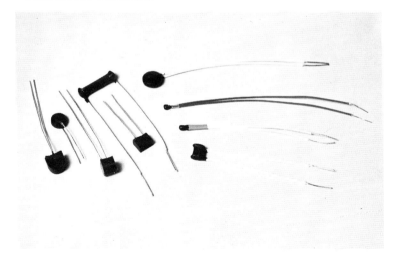

10. The photosensitive glass Fotoform can be precisely drilled by using ultraviolet light, heat, and acid. Here a technician removes a plate after it has been treated with acid. Subsequent heating will convert the glass to a glass ceramic, Fotoceram.

11. Steps in the production of a glass ultrasonic delay line.

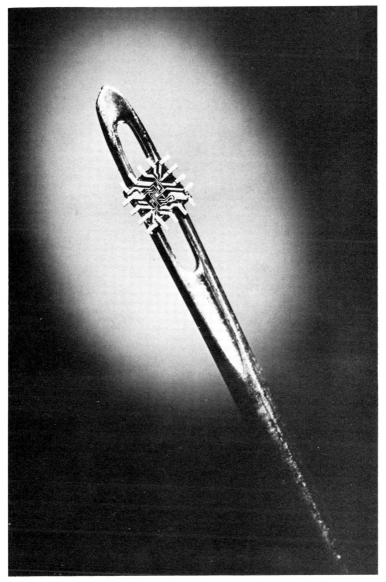

12. An example of miniaturization: An integrated circuit containing eighteen diodes, four transistors, and eight resistors, and only one-twentieth of an inch wide, can be balanced on the eye of a sewing needle.

13. Examples of the many ceramic-to-metal seals in use.

14. A ceramic thermoelectric generator. As shown on the voltmeter, the device converts the 1400°F. heat of an electric furnace into nearly 100 volts of electricity.

that this substance, instead of forming a perovskite, has a structure known as the *ilmenite* structure, named after the iron titanate, $Fe^{2+}TiO_3$. The ionic radii of this material also are shown in Table 7. Thus, of the alkaline

TABLE 7

SIZES OF IONS (Radii in angstrom units.) IN SOME $A^{2+}B^{4+}O^{2-}{}_3$ COMPOUNDS

Comp. No.	A Site	B Site	O Site
1	Mg^{2+} 0.67	Ti^{4+} 0.68	$O^{2-}{}_3$ 1.32
2	Ca^{2+} 0.99	Ti^{4+} 0.68	$O^{2-}{}_3$ 1.32
3	Sr^{2+} 1.12	Ti^{4+} 0.68	$O^{2-}{}_3$ 1.32
4	Ba^{2+} 1.34	Ti^{4+} 0.68	$O^{2-}{}_3$ 1.32
5	Fe^{2+} 0.74	Ti^{4+} 0.68	$O^{2-}{}_3$ 1.32

earth titanates, only $BaTiO_3$ has the correct ion sizes to be ferroelectric at room temperature.

Multiple Substitutions in the Perovskite Structure

We turn now to a discussion of more complex, *multiple* substitutions in the perovskite structure. (Similar substitutions can be made, of course, in the other ferroelectric structure types.) The possibility of putting such multiple-ion changes into effect raises the number of potential perovskites into the thousands. Typical substitutions in $BaTiO_3$, for example, are shown in Table 8. But a few "ground rules" should be noted: The ions in the A sites must have an average valence of 2+ and sizes close to those of Ba^{2+} or Sr^{2+}; that is, in or near the range 1.34 to 1.12 AU. Ions in the B sites must average 4+ and be about as small as Ti^{4+} (0.68 AU).

TABLE 8
EXAMPLES OF MULTIPLE SUBSTITUTIONS
IN $BaTiO_3$ AS AN $A^{2+}B^{4+}O^{2-}_3$ COMPOSITION
(Radii in angstrom units.)

Composition		Sites			
		A	A	B	B	O
(1)	$Ba_2Ti_2O_6$	Ba^{2+}	Ba^{2+}	Ti^{4+}	Ti^{4+}	O^{2-}_6
		1.34	1.34	0.68	0.68	1.32
(2)	$KLaTi_2O_6$	K^+	La^{3+}	Ti^{4+}	Ti^{4+}	O^{2-}_6
		1.33	1.14	0.68	0.68	1.32
(3)	Sr_2CrTaO_6	Sr^{2+}	Sr^{2+}	Cr^{3+}	Ta^{5+}	O^{2-}_6
		1.12	1.12	0.63	0.68	1.32
(4)	$BaKNbTiO_6$	Ba^{2+}	K^+	Nb^{5+}	Ti^{4+}	O^{2-}_6
		1.34	1.33	0.69	0.68	1.32

In writing $BaTiO_3$ as $Ba_2Ti_2O_6$ (to demonstrate the substitutions more clearly) we draw from reference material on line 1. If desired, we can replace all of the Ba^{2+} with K^+ and La^{3+}, which have the correct sizes to fit into the A sites, as shown on line 2. By using equal numbers of A^+ and A^{3+}, the average comes to the required A^{2+}. And similarly (line 3) we can use Cr^{3+} and Ta^{5+} to fill in for Ti^{4+} in the B sites. On line 4 we find an example of substituting K^+ for Ba^{2+} in the A sites. This leaves a cation charge deficiency in the A sites which is compensated for by introducing into the B sites the same number of ions of a higher charge (Nb^{5+}) as the number of K^+ present. These compositions and many more like them have been synthesized. They definitely possess the perovskite structure, but relatively few of them are also ferroelectric.

Fluoride (Model) Perovskites

To make "model" perovskite structures, one key method is to employ ions of the correct sizes in the A and B sites, but the ions should have only half the valence of the original. Models of oxides are made by using F^- in place of O^{2-}. In Table 9 several fluoride models of $BaTiO_3$ are shown. These fluorides are perovskites, but apparently they are not ferroelectric. It is remarkable, however, that the sizes of these selected lower-valent ions are so close to those of the oxidic material for which these fluoride compositions serve as a model.

TABLE 9

SUGGESTED FLUORIDE MODELS OF $BaTiO_3$.

(Ionic radii in angstrom units.)

Composition	A Site	B Site	O Site
$BaTiO_3$	Ba^{2+}	Ti^{4+}	O^{2-}_3
	1.34	0.68	1.32
$KMgF_3$	K^+	Mg^{2+}	F^-_3
	1.33	0.65	1.33
$KNiF_3$	K^+	Ni^{2+}	F^-_3
	1.33	0.69	1.33
$AgZnF_3$	Ag^+	Zn^{2+}	F^-_3
	1.26	0.74	1.33
$AgMgF_3$	Ag^+	Mg^{2+}	F^-_3
	1.26	0.65	1.33

SUMMARY

Ferroelectric materials are found among substances that have certain types of crystal symmetry. A ferroelectric has intrinsic, spontaneously formed dipoles which may be switched by an impressed voltage. Many ferroelectric compositions are inorganic, oxide-based materials which can be made into dense, hard ceramics. These ceramics, when electrically poled, become highly efficient in their ability to transform mechanical energy such as vibrations and changes in pressure and sound into electrical energy. In some cases the electrical energy thus created amounts to thousands of volts. Ferroelectric ceramics are equally effective, in a reverse direction, as a means of converting electrical signals into mechanical impulses.

The properties of ferroelectric ceramics depend to a large extent on their chemical compositions, that is, the sizes and valence of ions in the various crystal sites. These characteristics are influenced strongly by the quality and microstructure of the ceramic.

Many people consider only that ceramics are very inert materials, chemically and physically stable, good for making containers, and that they have the ability to resist high temperatures. It is not so well-known that ferroelectric ceramics can also serve very effectively in electrical-mechanical conversions. Ceramic scientists have resorted extensively to the concepts of crystal chemistry in their effort to understand the phenomena involved, improve the performance of such ceramics, and tailor ferroelectrics to meet new specifications. As time goes on they can be expected to apply increasingly the principles of solid-state chemistry and physics to their work.

Chapter VII

DIELECTRICS:
THE ENERGY HOARDERS

In working with electronics, it is often necessary to block completely the flow of an electric current, or to permit a controlled amount of current to pass, or to store energy for various purposes. Three types of ceramic materials are used to accomplish these results. Materials that block electrons are called *insulators;* the ones that pass controlled amounts are *resistors,* and those that store electrical energy rather than transmit it are known as *dielectrics.* Devices in which dielectrics are used are called *capacitors* or *insulators,* depending on their functions in the circuit.

A dielectric is a material in which it is possible to produce and maintain an electric field with little or no additional energy supplied from outside sources. A vacuum is the only known perfect dielectric. Insulating materials are imperfect dielectrics, because when they are subjected to applied voltage they may show *absorption* and *conduction currents* in addition to the *displacement* or *charging currents* seen also in vacuums.

The difference between a poor insulator and a high-valued resistor may be only a matter of the degree of current passage. Thus, a material that is a poor insulator permits a very small but measurable amount of current flow; it is commonly said to "leak" the electrical energy stored in it. On the other hand, a good resistor will deliberately permit the passage of the amount of current which it was designed to deliver.

DIELECTRIC CONSTANT AND
DIELECTRIC STRENGTH

When an electric circuit contains two surfaces or areas of conducting material (such as two plates of copper, aluminum, or silver) separated by a dielectric, that is, a nonconductor, any difference in potential—any voltage between the two surfaces—puts a strain on the intervening dielectric. Some of the electricity, in attempting to pass from one conductor to the other, is stored. This "sandwich" composed of two conductors and an interposed dielectric is said to have *electrostatic capacitance:* the ability to hold and store electricity. A device in which the sandwich arrangement is deliberately designed for such a purpose is called a *capacitor.* An older term, *condenser,* is still occasionally used. In general, the greater the voltage applied, the more electricity is stored in the capacitor. (A ceramic capacitor is shown in Figure 9.)

Early condensers were made of two plates of metal with air between. Paper, mica, glass, and other dielectrics were used later in capacitors. To calculate how much energy the capacitor would store it was necessary to know how effective the chosen dielectric would be. In this way the term *dielectric constant,* or energy-storing ability of the material, came into general use. This storage capacity is compared to that of the same thickness of vacuum, which is given the value of one. As a matter of fact, the dielectric constant of dry air at $0°$ C and standard atmospheric pressure is 1.0006, so that, for example, we may think of the dielectric constant of a ceramic material as telling us how much more efficient than air that material is when placed between the plates of a capacitor.

So we see that dielectrics, in addition to being essentially nonconductors, also are "energy hoarders" in proportion to their dielectric constant.

In most insulators, the electric displacement (charg-

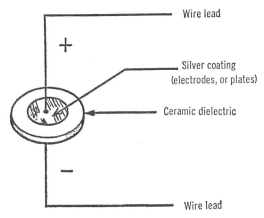

+

−

Wire lead

Silver coating
(electrodes, or plates)

Ceramic dielectric

Wire lead

Figure 9. Ceramic disc capacitor. The capacity is directly
proportional to the area of the electrodes (plates) and the
dielectric constant of the ceramic, and inversely proportional to the thickness of the ceramic.

ing) increases in direct proportion to the applied field.
These are called *linear dielectrics.* For many of the materials with high dielectric constant, however, the displacement increases in a nonlinear (not a straight line)
manner, and these are referred to as *nonlinear dielectrics.* Both classes of materials will be described in this
chapter.

Another property besides dielectric constant is important if one wishes to store the greatest amount of energy
in the smallest volume. It is the ability of the material
to hold energy at a very high voltage; this is true because
the quantity of energy stored increases with the applied
field.

The number of volts per unit of distance between conductors, through the dielectric, is known as the *voltage
gradient.* We usually express this in volts per centimeter,
volts per inch, or volts per mil (thousandth of an inch).
If a dielectric is subjected to a voltage gradient that is
too intense, the strain resulting from the ions and electrons trying to get through may exceed the *dielectric*

strength. In such a case, the dielectric material begins to break down, and the passage of current is allowed. Therefore, in choosing a suitable dielectric material for making a capacitor, we need to know both the dielectric constant and the dielectric strength.

For example, one material may have an outstanding dielectric strength but a low dielectric constant. Another material may have almost unbelievably high dielectric constant with only moderate dielectric strength.

Keep in mind that dielectric constant is a measurement of electrical storage capacity; dielectric strength refers to a material's ability to prevent the passage of current. The former is a ratio, or number relative to the dielectric capacity of a vacuum; the latter measurement (dielectric strength) is stated in terms of the maximum voltage gradient (volts per mil, etc.) that a given material can sustain without disruptive discharge. (See Table 10 for comparative values of several commonly used dielectric materials.)

DEVELOPMENT OF CAPACITOR MATERIALS

In the early days of radio receivers a person could tune in the various broadcasting stations by turning the knob of a "variable condenser." This was a capacitor with two sets of closely spaced parallel metal plates. One set was stationary and the other was capable of sliding in and out between the plates of the first set. The plates were not allowed to come in contact with each other; this provided an air gap of constant thickness but variable area. We still occasionally see variable air-gap capacitors today.

Some capacitors in the early radio sets were made of mica, oiled paper, and other materials with dielectric constant values under 10. Mica's outstanding merit is its high dielectric strength, and this made it a critical material in the early days of World War II. A plate of electrical-grade mica one-thousandth of an inch thick

TABLE 10
REPRESENTATIVE PROPERTIES OF
COMMONLY USED DIELECTRIC MATERIALS,
LISTED FOR PURPOSES OF COMPARISON

Material	Dielectric Constant	Dielectric Strength, Volts per Mil
Mica	2.5–7.3	125–5500
Rubber	2.0–3.5	400–1200
Phenolic resin	7.5	2000
Glass		
Fused Silica	3.5–4.1	400, at 50° C
Borosilicate	4.0–5.7	
Soda lime	7.2	
Soda lead	8.4–9.5	
Ceramics		
Alumina	4.5–9.5	40–400
Beryllia	6.0–6.5	250–300
Rutile	15–110	50–300
Forsterite	6.2	Over 200
Cordierite	5.8	Over 200
Steatite	6.0–6.5	Over 200
Electrical porc.	4.4–7.0	100–400
Zircon	8.8	Over 200
Titanates	15–12,000	100–300

can withstand an electrical potential of several thousand volts.

Studies in the latter part of the 1930s led to the introduction of capacitors made of ceramic bodies containing mainly rutile (titanium dioxide, TiO_2). These had dielectric constants of 80 to 100—greater than any values previously known. This touched off a search for ceramic dielectrics with even higher dielectric constants. The rutile-based devices filled an immediate need for capacitors in the field of entertainment electronics, however— radio and television receivers, record players, public-address systems, etc.—and they are still used for this purpose today.

In 1943, barium titanate emerged as a new capacitor

material; it had a dielectric constant of 1200 to 1500. This was considered a spectacular development. Today, modifications of barium titanate are used in making ceramic capacitor materials with dielectric constants of 12,000 and higher. These have great value in the miniaturization of capacitors.

For example, as I write this, I am looking at a small "shirt-pocket" transistor radio. I can see ten ceramic capacitors in this radio receiver, and still others may be hidden. Four are marked 0.01 μF (microfarad); one is 0.05 μF; and five are 0.005 μF. (A farad is a large unit of capacitance; it is the capacity of an electrical condenser, or capacitor, which gives a potential difference of one volt when charged with one coulomb—the coulomb being the quantity of electricity transferred by a current of one ampere in one second. A microfarad is one millionth of a farad.)

These tiny capacitors are flat discs of ceramic, probably with silver electrodes, and are coated with a plastic for protection. Even with the plastic coating, the discs are only about ⅜ inch in diameter. Assuming a standard thickness of ceramic, the 0.01 μF capacitors presumably are made of a material having a dielectric constant of about 5000 to 7000. If these capacitors were made with the same thickness of the best material available before 1943 (a rutile ceramic with dielectric constant of 80), they would be more than 3½ inches across.

Looking back farther, if my little capacitors had to be made of sheet mica (with a dielectric constant of 7), the diameter of the discs—still assuming the same thickness—would grow to about 15½ inches. We can hardly imagine a pocket-size radio with capacitors made even of rutile ceramics. As a matter of fact, this is one of the reasons why such radios were unknown in 1940.

A well-known ceramic material with a high dielectric constant is an "89-10-1 body." It consists of 89 percent barium titanate (by weight), 10 percent calcium zirconate, and 1 percent magnesium zirconate. When blended, shaped, dried, and ceramically fired to a dense, impervious polycrystalline wafer, such a mix has a dielectric constant above 5000. The constant tends to reach a broad maximum in the range between 10° to 30° C (50° to 86° F). Another formulation—80 percent barium titanate, 10 percent calcium zirconate, and 10 percent strontium titanate—has an even higher dielectric constant. This material regularly can be fired to a room-temperature dielectric constant of 9400 to 9500.

NONLINEAR DIELECTRICS FOR CAPACITORS

Ferroelectric ceramics (see Chapter VI) frequently are used in special capacitors for their energy-storage capabilities. The reason is twofold: (1) Dielectric constant tends to be higher and (2) the dielectric constant can be changed by varying the applied field, or the temperature, or both. Such materials are called nonlinear dielectrics because of their *voltage dependence*. Meanwhile, their *temperature dependence* works as follows: The dielectric constant reaches a peak at the Curie temperature of the material and drops off with both increasing or decreasing temperatures from this point. A typical dielectric constant-temperature curve, that for barium titanate, is shown in Figure 10. The dielectric constant of barium titanate reaches a maximum at 120° C—its Curie point. Likewise, the highest constants of related dielectrics, lead titanate and lead metaniobate, for example, are found at their respective Curie temperatures of 480° and 570° C. This type of data gives the ceramic engineer an important guide for tailoring his capacitor materials.

In practice, barium titanate is often used as the major ingredient in temperature-compensating and voltage-tunable capacitors. Its sensitivity to changes in temperature and applied voltage can be modified extensively by making what may seem to be minor changes in chemical composition. Some of these controls will be noted briefly in the following paragraphs.

In radio circuits, the characteristics of various components may change appreciably as the temperature

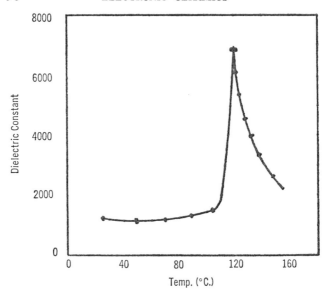

Figure 10. Dielectric constant of barium titanate as a function of temperature.

changes. This is seen when a radio set "warms up"—at such time the properties of the resistors and related devices often change. To balance this effect, the radio engineer uses capacitors that have an opposite effect, that is, special ceramic dielectrics that compensate for the temperature variations of the other components of the circuit.

The ceramist—depending on where he sets the Curie point relative to the operating temperature of the electronic circuit—is able to produce a material in which the capacitance will either increase or decrease as the temperature is raised. Such materials are said to have either a positive or a negative *temperature coefficient of capacitance.*

One of the ways to accomplish this is to add a material known as a "Curie point shifter." Strontium titanate is one of the most widely used Curie point shifters for

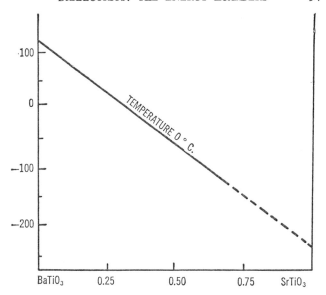

Figure 11. Curie temperatures of barium-strontium titanate compositions.

barium titanate. Figure 11 shows how the Curie temperature of barium titanate is lowered by additions of strontium titanate. This concept is further illustrated in Figure 12. Assume that enough strontium titanate has been added to barium titanate to give a material (Composition A) having a Curie temperature (T_1) well below the range of temperatures within which a circuit is to be operated. Such a composition provides the dielectric for a capacitor having negative temperature coefficient of capacitance. Another material, Composition B, containing much less strontium titanate and having a Curie temperature (T_2) above the operating temperature of the circuit, would have a positive temperature coefficient of capacitance. The number and kind of temperature-compensating capacitors used in a circuit will depend, of course, on the temperature sensitivity of the other components of the circuit.

Equally important is the fact that nonlinear dielectrics

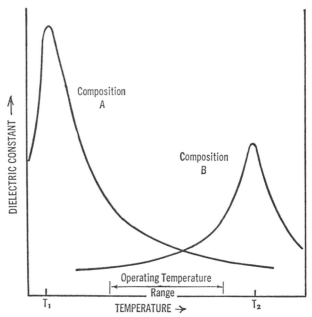

Figure 12. Illustration of the concept of two ferroelectric compositions, one with negative and the other with positive temperature coefficient of dielectric constant within the operating temperature range of an electronic circuit.

are sensitive to the voltage applied, and the ceramic scientist takes advantage of this sensitivity. By varying a *biasing voltage,* a separate dc field applied to the material, one may change its dielectric constant and hence its capacitance. What we have, in fact, is a "voltage-tuned" capacitor.

If one needs to tune an electronic circuit in an inaccessible location—where it would not be feasible to turn a knob, for example—one remote-control method that will work is the adjustment of a nonlinear capacitor by changing a biasing voltage. In the reverse direction, changes in the capacitance of a nonlinear capacitor can be used to detect variations in electrical field, and this is an important feature in certain voltage-control devices.

The nonlinearity of a barium titanate capacitor material can be reduced, that is, its stability at various temperatures and voltages can be *increased*, by the addition of small amounts of certain stannates, among other ways. About 10 percent of bismuth stannate, $Bi_2(SnO_3)_3$, used as a "Curie peak leveler," will make the dielectric constant vs. temperature curve of barium titanate essentially "flat" from 20° to 100° C. Figure 13 shows this relation-

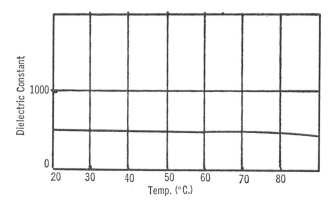

Figure 13. Dielectric constant vs. temperature, showing almost straight-line relationship when barium titanate contains about 10 percent bismuth stannate.

ship. Bismuth stannate is very insensitive to changes in applied voltage, as shown in Figure 14, while 13 percent, added to barium titanate, helps control the voltage sensitivity of the latter material.

On the other hand, the addition of, for example, 10 percent of copper stannate, $CuSnO_3$, can greatly increase the nonlinearity of barium titanate, so much so that by the time the biasing field has been increased to 20 volts per mil the capacitance is down by approximately 75 percent. (This also is indicated in Figure 14.) Here we have an example of a material suitable for a voltage-tunable capacitor.

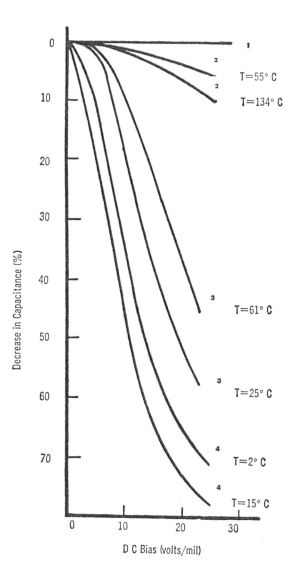

LOW-LOSS DIELECTRICS AND INSULATORS

We will turn now to an important group of *linear ceramic dielectrics*. These are materials which generally have lower dielectric constant values and are characterized by very low electrical losses at high frequencies. In other words, they have high electrical resistance and show very little loss of energy (for example, they do not readily become heated) under the influence of frequencies even as high as those in the microwave range.

The linear ceramics are used primarily for electrical insulation in such electronic components as coil forms and vacuum tube sockets, bases and envelopes. They are used also as substrates for microelectronics (see Chapter IX). These materials are especially valuable where high operating temperatures are a factor along with other requirements.

Electrical grade porcelain was the principal ceramic insulating material until about 1930. It served well at lower frequencies and still is widely used in power-line insulators and in the distribution of electrical energy. As frequencies were progressively increased, the need for higher insulation resistance and low electrical losses spurred development of other types of ceramics. Commonly used for various purposes are dense porcelainlike bodies of steatite, $MgO \cdot SiO_2$; forsterite, $2MgO \cdot SiO_2$; cordierite, $2MgO \cdot 2Al_2O_3 \cdot 5SiO_2$; zircon, $ZrO_2 \cdot SiO_2$; alumina, Al_2O_3; and beryllia, BeO. Boron nitride, BN, a relatively new material, shows considerable promise in this high-frequency, low-loss area.

Forsterite ceramics have low dielectric losses, but their resistance to rapid temperature changes is poor because

Figure 14. Capacitance change vs. direct current bias for various compositions (at a frequency of 10 mHz): (1) bismuth stannate; (2) 87 percent barium titanate, 13 percent bismuth stannate; (3) 79 percent barium titanate, 21 percent lead stannate; (4) 90 percent barium titanate, 10 percent copper stannate (after Coffeen).

they expand a great deal when heated. This same high thermal expansion is valuable in making ceramic-to-metal seals with various useful metals such as iron alloys and titanium, however, because the expansion characteristics in the ceramics and metals are similar. Beryllia ceramics are used in electronic devices when high thermal conductivity is required to dissipate the heat generated by closely spaced electronic components. The thermal conductivity of a dense beryllia ceramic is about ten times that of dense alumina.

HIGH-TEMPERATURE INSULATORS

The electrical resistivity of oxidic materials decreases as the temperature is raised; thus, it is common practice to classify insulator materials by the temperature at which their electrical resistivity drops to one megohm (one million ohms) per centimeter. This is known as the Te value, and it is still a high value of resistivity compared to that of a conductor; it is nearly a million million (10^{12}) times that of copper at room temperature. Te values of materials we have discussed range as follows: cordierite, 500° C; steatite, 850° C; zircon, 870° C; forsterite, 900° C; 99.5 percent alumina, 1100° C; and 99.5 percent beryllia, 1250° C.

Some of the recently developed electronic ceramics display remarkable high-temperature insulation characteristics. Two examples of these devices include:

(1) Small insulator spacers used in the manufacture of vacuum tubes. These are generally composed of a material with high alumina content.

(2) Vacuum tubes of the "all-ceramic" type which operate at temperatures well above the highest at which glass and metal tubes can be used and far above the top safe temperatures for transistors. These are made with a forsterite envelope; they are small and rugged, and electronic circuits using these tubes, along with high-temperature resistors and capacitors developed for the purpose,

have been operated successfully above 500° C. One of these tubes is shown in Plate 8.

SUBSTRATES

We will discuss microminiaturization of electronic circuits in Chapter IX. It should be pointed out that the tiny circuits of dielectrics and insulators have to be mounted on *something,* however, just as the large electronic components of a conventional radio set are mounted on an aluminum chassis. Dense alumina ceramics, usually in the form of small, thin wafers, are now frequently used for the smaller devices. Alumina has good electrical and mechanical properties and is available at a reasonable cost. If it becomes necessary to carry away large amounts of heat, we can use beryllia ceramics as *substrates* (bases or carrying devices). For greater smoothness, some of these small ceramic wafers are glazed before being sold.

RESISTORS

Resistors may be linear or nonlinear. In a linear resistor, the resistivity remains constant and the amount of current flowing is proportional to the applied field, or voltage. On the other hand, in a nonlinear type, the resistivity depends on the voltage used; in other words, the resistivity is a function of the field, and the amount of current passed is not directly proportional to the voltage across the resistor material.

Resistors also may be linear or nonlinear with respect to temperature.

THE VARISTOR

The varistor is a nonlinear resistor sensitive to changes in voltage. Varistors are used for sensing and regulating voltages and for protecting circuits from overloads. They help protect rectifiers, capacitors, and other electronic components. A common type of ceramic varistor consists of silicon carbide granules blended in varying ratios with graphite and clay to give a range of properties. If such a ceramic is sintered in a reducing atmosphere, the clay serves as the bond.

THE THERMISTOR

A tiny piece of electronic ceramic is probably responsible for telling you the temperature of your automobile engine. Such a ceramic is called a thermistor—a heat-sensitive resistor. The classical thermistor was first developed about twenty years ago; it had a large negative temperature coefficient (NTC) of resistance, that is, its resistance dropped with climbing temperature. Modified indium antimonide (InSb) and chemically modified mixed oxides of such metals as chromium, manganese, iron, cobalt, and nickel were used in the NTC thermistors.

More recently, thermistors with positive temperature coefficient (PTC) have been developed. These are called PTC thermistors, or posistors, to distinguish them from the earlier NTC type. PTC thermistors are made by adding small amounts (0.1 to 1.5 percent) of such oxides as lanthanum, bismuth, thorium, yttrium, etc., to barium titanate and its solid solutions. The resistivity of barium titanate is reduced from a million million (10^{12}) ohm-centimeters to only 10 to 1000 ohm-cm when these modifiers are introduced into either the A or B sites of the ABO_3 crystal lattice. The positive temperature coefficient of the resulting material causes its resistivity to increase at a high rate—on the order of 15 percent for each degree centigrade of temperature. There is also a very large and sudden rise in resistivity as the material goes through its Curie point. Again, by substituting Sr^{2+} for some of the Ba^{2+} ions the Curie temperature can be lowered; and by substituting Pb^{2+} it can be raised, thus allowing the engineer to tailor thermistors to cover a wide variety of temperatures.

With a thermistor it is a simple matter to measure the temperature of a car radiator or cylinder block. (The latter is more commonly checked.) Current from the battery usually is fed through the temperature-sensitive resistor and then to a current-measuring meter (calibrated to read directly in degrees Fahrenheit) on the instrument panel of the vehicle.

A fishing thermometer may seem a peculiar place for an electronic ceramic; an extremely sensitive temperature indicator is available, however, to detect the exact depth at which water temperature suddenly changes. The angler drops his hook or line to this spot, which supposedly is where the fish wait. The fishing thermometer is simply a thermistor on a fine copper wire connected to a meter in the boat.

Thermistors also are used to protect television receivers, home radios, and hi-fi sets from voltage surges that might otherwise damage them. They are effective, as well, in air-conditioning units, thermostats, and in other places where temperature measurements and compensations are needed. Typical PTC thermistor ceramics are shown in Plate 9(a). After having leads attached and a protective cover added, the finished thermistors look like those in Plate 9(b).

A HIGH-TEMPERATURE STABLE RESISTOR

One characteristic of metals is that their resistivity goes up with temperature; yet, as we know, the resistivity of ceramic oxides tends to go down with additional heat. By blending the two materials—metals and ceramic oxides —into a single resistive material, a compensated, or temperature-stable, resistor can be made.

A high-temperature resistor has been developed using this scheme, and by enclosing the tailored material in a small, thin-walled, gas-tight tube of alumina ceramic sealed at both ends with metal caps which serve as electrodes. This protects the resistor material from dirt and moisture and helps prevent the changes in resistivity that might come if the resistive mix were allowed to oxidize at the high temperature of use.

SUMMARY

Some ceramic materials either partially or completely impede the flow of electrons in electric circuits. These materials are based on the concept of the dielectric: a material in which it is possible to establish an electrical potential, or field, that will not leak away. The better dielectrics, that is, materials featuring low electrical loss at high frequency (and usually lower dielectric constant) are used as insulators in electronic circuits. Dielectrics can be modified to allow the passage of limited amounts of current; in this way they become resistors. Resistors can be made by other means, however, such as by winding lengths of fine wire on a ceramic core.

Ceramic dielectric and resistor materials may be linear or nonlinear, and all gradations between. The linear materials have properties that change in a uniform way with variations in temperature and/or voltage, while the nonlinear compositions are nonuniform in their reactions to such changes.

Chapter VIII

GLASS IN ELECTRONICS

Glass is an important electronic ceramic material. Many glass compositions have very good electrical resistivity and dielectric strength, and are thus useful both as substrates and as "envelopes."

About 90 percent of all glass produced in the United States is a type called "soda lime." This is made from a mixture of about 70 percent silica sand (silicon dioxide, SiO_2) and the oxides of sodium and calcium, which are commonly added to the batch in the form of the carbonates. The name soda lime is derived from sodium oxide or carbonate (soda) and calcium oxide or carbonate (lime).

Soda-lime glass is used for windows, bottles, drinking glasses, and light bulbs, but it is not very satisfactory for electronic applications. It is too sensitive to the effect of moisture, and its electrical resistivity is too low.

Many other types of glass are available, however. Almost every chemical element has been used in making glass; in fact, some of the more complex glasses contain twenty to thirty ingredients. The Corning Glass Works alone is said to have more than one hundred thousand formulas for different varieties of glass.

The glasses used in electronics tend to have a lower alkali (especially soda) content than container glass. As a consequence, the electronic types generally require a higher temperature for melting and thus can withstand greater heat in service. Indeed, a glass made by fusing pure silica contains no alkali at all. This is known as fused silica, and sometimes, erroneously, it is called fused quartz.

Whereas in previous chapters we have referred frequently to the crystal structure of the electronically active materials, we should note that glass is an "amorphous" material. That is to say, it belongs to that class of materials that have no crystal structure as such. The constituent atoms pack themselves not quite randomly, but at characteristic average distances. There is a limited amount of order, but the structure lacks the precision of distances and angles and the repetition of geometric arrangements that characterize a crystal. In fact, although glass is a solid at room temperature it lacks crystallinity to such an extent that some investigators have likened it to a liquid.

There does not seem to be any one glass composition that is used exclusively for electronics. Rather, any glass that is pure enough and has the correct properties for the intended use in this field is likely to be classed as an electronic grade glass.

GLASS FOR CAPACITORS

A scientist must consider many factors in selecting a glass for capacitors. Pure silica glass has the lowest dielectric constant: about 3.8. The dielectric constant is raised by the addition of various other oxides, but this also may bring unsatisfactory effects such as high electrical losses in fields of alternating current, or undesirable conductivity in direct-current fields.

In some respects, dielectric strength is even more important than dielectric constant. This is true because the amount of energy that can be stored in a capacitor varies not only directly with the dielectric constant but also with the *square* of the dielectric strength.

A potash-lead glass is often used in glass capacitors. This type has a dielectric constant of about 8.8; it also features high dielectric strength and low electrical loss. It can be drawn as a thin, flexible ribbon about one mil thick, and it matches the coefficient of thermal expansion of the aluminum foil used for its electrodes. Alternate layers of glass ribbon and aluminum foil are sealed together at a high temperature to form rugged units. Leads are attached, and a stack of such units is then fused into a glass case.

Such fixed-glass capacitors are produced in a range of values from about 0.5 PF (picofarad) to about 150 μF (microfarads) and are designed for working voltages up to 6000 volts. (A microfarad is one-millionth of a farad, and a picofarad is one-millionth of a microfarad; in other words, a picofarad is 1×10^{-12} farad.)

GLASS CERAMICS

A new and valuable group of glasses can be shaped by conventional glass-forming methods, then transformed into polycrystalline, porcelainlike materials by heating. The secret of controlling this conversion process lies in the time-temperature schedule selected for the heat treatment. At one temperature—800° C, for instance—a nucleating agent, present in the molten glass, precipitates as finely dispersed droplets, particles, or nuclei. At a higher temperature, such as 1200° C, crystals grow on the dispersed nucleating phase. Such a schedule is shown in Figure 15.

Certain special glasses do not need a separate agent, or material, for producing nuclei. In these the particles form spontaneously at a given temperature. This temperature is usually different from that of crystal growth; thus we can state the control procedure as follows:

The longer we hold the glass at the temperature of nuclei formation, the more of the particles we produce; the longer we keep the glass at the heat of crystal growth, the larger the crystals become. This is an oversimplification, but it means, in a general way, that we can produce a glass containing few crystals or many crystals, as desired, and the crystals may be either large or small. A completely devitrified or converted glass may be almost entirely crystalline. Pyroceram—made by the Corning Glass Works —is the name given to a group of glasses produced according to this basic scheme. Pyroceram is mentioned here because it is such a well-known example of glass ceramics. Articles made of glass ceramics commonly are stronger and harder than the glass from which they were converted. Pyroceram Code 9606 was specifically developed to give uniform electrical properties at microwave frequencies and elevated temperatures, for missile radomes.

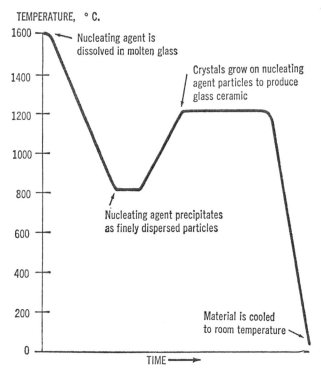

TEMPERATURE, ° C.

Figure 15. Time-temperature sequence followed in making a glass ceramic.

Older but less well-known is Corning's Fotoform glass, introduced in 1953. When exposed to light and then heat-treated, this clear glass produces a three-dimensional photographic pattern or image that can be dissolved in hydrofluoric acid. By exposing the glass through a photographic negative or a mask (a screen to cover or hide selected portions), it is therefore possible to "chemically machine" intricate designs in and through the glass. This etched glass is extensively used in the electronics industry for making transistor wafers, vacuum tube spacers, fine-mesh screens with up to 360,000 holes per square inch, and boards for printed circuits. Further heat treatment will convert the etched glass into a strong, opaque, brown glass ceramic called Fotoceram. Because of its greater strength and electrical resistance, Fotoceram frequently is the preferred type for electronic purposes. (See Plate 10.)

CONDUCTING AND SEMICONDUCTING GLASSES

Extensive research now under way on semiconducting glasses may lead to many new applications. Until recently, semiconductor investigations were carried out only with crystalline materials.

Actually, the electrical properties of glasses have been studied for more than a hundred years. Most glasses, as we have pointed out, contain appreciable quantities of alkali oxides, principally soda (sodium oxide, Na_2O). We know that the alkali ions move through the glass as "charge carriers." This type of electrical conduction is called *ionic*. There is also another means of carrying a current through glass, called *electronic* conduction. In this method, the electrons themselves travel through the glass in a series of jumps rather than being carried by moving ions.

For some uses, electrically conducting glass is desired, and one can do things to the glass to enhance this property. Generally, we prefer to make the electronic conduction easier, because this provides a more stable, uniform, long-lived level of current passage. Ionic conduction is inherently unstable since under long service most of the charge carriers will be used up and the ability to conduct will become diminished. That is, when enough of the easily moved alkali ions have migrated to the cathode (negative electrode) the number of available carriers becomes less and consequently the resistance of the glass must increase.

If we wish to *diminish* the conductivity or to have a high electrical resistivity, however, we produce a glass that does not contain ions that can contribute significantly either to ionic conduction or to electronic conduction.

The name *electronically conducting glass* has been given to one type of specially tailored glass. To make this type, a glass containing lead oxide is reduced by heating in hydrogen so as to give the surface a thin layer of metallic lead. When grounded, this layer can be used to prevent the buildup of electrostatic charges in high-voltage glass devices such as X-ray tubes.

In a slightly different approach, we can deposit a transparent layer of tin oxide, SnO_2, on a glass surface. When a voltage is applied to such a layer, or film, a current flows and heat is generated. This effect is useful in decorative panels for heating small rooms, or in windshields, where it prevents condensation (fogging) and provides de-icing.

We have known in recent years, particularly since 1961, that electronic conduction is possible in the *bulk* of a glass, that is, through the glass itself rather than along the surface. By adjusting the glass composition, we can make *electronic conduction* predominate over *ionic conduction*. The mechanism of electronic conduction here is similar to that in silicon and germanium—the well-known semiconductors—and glasses of this type are called *semiconducting glasses*.

Semiconducting glasses typically have low electrical resistivity, ranging from 500 ohm centimeters upward, and negative temperature coefficient of resistance. Some of these glasses have an unusually high rate of change in resistance with temperature variations, and apparently are suitable for thermistor applications.

The early semiconducting glasses were based on a composition of vanadium pentoxide and phosphorus pentoxide (V_2O_5 and P_2O_5). By introducing rather large quantities of oxides that are semiconductors we can improve the semiconducting qualities. For example, iron oxide (FeO), cobalt oxide (CoO), and manganese oxide (MnO) are commonly used oxides for this purpose. Meanwhile, other semiconducting glasses have been found in compositions containing sodium oxide, boric oxide, and titanium dioxide (Na_2O-B_2O_3-TiO_2).

GLASS SUBSTRATES

In Chapter VII we discussed the use of alumina wafers as substrates (devices that serve as carriers or bases) for microelectronic circuits. Glass sheets also are used for this purpose. Such sheets are made of thin, optical-quality glass with very smooth surface finishes, and they normally range in thickness between 0.0020 inch (2 mils) and 0.0240 inch (24 mils). The glass is often cut by the manufacturer into rectangles, squares, and circles, ready for the depositing of tiny circuits. It can also be obtained in larger sheets which are then cut by the user.

OTHER SPECIAL USES OF GLASS

Fused silica glass will transmit an ultrasonic signal (above the audible range of the human ear) with practically no loss, or scattering, of the sound waves. This property has led to its use in *ultrasonic delay lines*. A delay line serves to hold back an electrical signal for a short period of time. In color television, delay lines permit three pictures, in three primary colors, to be transmitted one after the other. The first and second pictures can be delayed until the third arrives, and all three are flashed on the fluorescent screen simultaneously. There are many uses, in radars and computers, for delay lines offering longer delay times.

In these devices an electronic signal is converted by a transducer (see Chapter VI) into an ultrasonic signal that travels through the glass until it is picked up by a second transducer and converted back into an electrical impulse. Relatively long delay times are obtained by causing the sonic signal to pass repeatedly back and forth through the glass, being reflected from face to face in a precisely ground, many-sided prism.

Although some early delay lines were made of long lengths of wire, these are no longer used for this purpose. An electrical signal passes along a wire at about the speed of light. A sound signal travels at different rates in different materials, but of the order of 1/100,000 of the speed of light. Accordingly, a sound signal of the type used in an ultrasonic delay line would require about forty microseconds to travel through four inches of the glass shown in Plate 11. To create the same amount of delay of an electrical impulse, using wire alone, one would need nearly forty thousand feet of wire.

If a glass ultrasonic delay line is to be used in a location where there is a considerable variation in temperature, fused silica is at a disadvantage. The time delay of fused silica changes by about only eighty parts per million for each degree centigrade change in temperature, but this is considered too much for some uses. Therefore, a special glass has been tailored in which the time delay varies by only 0.5 part per million (or perhaps less) per degree change in temperature. The production of an ultrasonic delay line of this type starts with the preparation of a round pressed blank of "Zero TC" glass, as shown in Plate 11. The disc is then ground to an exacting configuration, after which the transducers and leads are attached.

LOW TEMPERATURE GLASSES

One group of inorganic glasses is so soft it is almost like taffy, and not at all brittle. It melts at such low temperatures we can dip temperature-sensitive electronic components into it as a means of protecting the devices. These glasses are composed of sulphur, arsenic, and thallium—a rather dangerously poisonous combination—but they seem to offer good electrical properties. They melt (depending on the ratios of their ingredients) between about 150° C and 500° C. During melting, however, it is necessary to surround the heated container with nitrogen or some other inert gas in order to prevent oxidation. One of the key advantages of a glass with a low melting point is the fact that its annealing temperature, the point at which strains are relieved, also is low. This group of glasses can, therefore, frequently be dropped to the floor without cracking, because even at room temperature they are above their annealing temperature and hence are not very brittle.

Chapter IX

MICROELECTRONICS AND
OTHER APPLICATIONS

We will discuss briefly in this chapter a number of materials, devices, and techniques, some of which are relatively new and dramatically different. The subjects include *microelectronics; seals* and *metallizing; superconducting* materials; *photoconductive* and *electroluminescent* materials; *thermoelectric* materials; and *vacuum tubes* versus *transistors.*

MICROELECTRONICS

Dick Tracy's two-way wrist television set is not far removed from reality, thanks to microelectronics. It will come as a part of the evolutionary thrust which began several decades ago when manufacturers began attempting to *miniaturize* and *microminiaturize* their electronic components, devices, and circuits.

The transistor, introduced in 1948, was a major step in this direction. But even earlier, the electronics industry had managed to shrink the vacuum tube from the size of a light bulb to an object no bigger than a peanut (as we noted in Chapter I). Today the transistor does many of the jobs of a vacuum tube in a functional area sometimes only a little larger than the period at the end of this sentence.

Microelectronics involves the placing of integrated networks of separate and tiny components (resistors, capacitors, transistors, diodes), along with their interconnections, on various bases or *substrates*. These microminiaturized circuits offer lower costs, reduced volume and weight, and improved reliability and performance. The value of such manufactured circuits has roughly doubled every year since 1962, as seen by these totals: 1962— 17 million dollars; 1963—32 million dollars; 1964—63 million dollars; 1965–137 million dollars. A microelectronic circuit is seen in Plate 12.

Instead of the old assembly lines for conventional electronic circuits, where rows of girls plugged components into metal chassis, we now often have a series of *vacuum chambers* and *evaporation stations*. In these the layers of components and their interconnections are laid down by "vacuum evaporation" and "vacuum sputtering" of various metals, oxides, etc., through intricate masks.

Vacuum evaporation and vacuum sputtering are closely related methods of thin film deposition. In the former, the material to be deposited is heated in a high vacuum by hot wires or by other means to such a temperature that it evaporates, and then condenses on a nearby cooler substrate. The vacuum is of the order of 5×10^{-5} torr (millimeters of mercury), that is, about one ten-millionth of an atmosphere of pressure. Some materials that are difficult to evaporate—high-temperature metals, alloys, semiconductors, and dielectrics—can be conveniently sputtered. Sputtering is a process in which the source material (target) is bombarded with charged gas ions; this erodes atoms or groups of atoms from the target and deposits them on an adjacent substrate. The gas may be inert, such as argon, or reactive, as nitrogen or oxygen. The gas pressure during sputtering is very low, usually between 1 and 40×10^{-3} torr.

Selected etching and precision machining are included in the process. Miniature circuits and their components also may be deposited by "printing" procedures—modified silk-screening and photolithographic techniques. Because the films deposited by these techniques are very thin, the products are known as *thin-film* circuits. (See Figure 16.)

In such circuits, the number of components per square inch of substrate is steadily increasing. One popular procedure is to print the components on tiny wafers of glass or ceramic. The wafers, all the same size, are called *modular substrates*. These can be assembled in stacks to make up the total circuit. Microcircuits are especially valuable when a piece of equipment needs many similar circuits—a computer, for example.

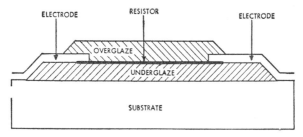

Figure 16. The structure of the thin-film resistor (schematic).

Closely related to thin-film microelectronics is the manufacture of thick-film microcircuits. The process here is very similar to the silk-screen method of printing permanent labels on bottles. Many soft-drink bottles, and some milk bottles, are labeled this way. By rubbing your fingers over the letters you can feel that they are slightly raised.

In making thick-film microcircuits, the circuits are built up in layers through the addition of the appropriate raw material in paste form squeezed through a series of masks, usually made of stainless steel screens. The substrate is likely to be an alumina ceramic 10 to 60 mils thick, depending on the size and intended use of the circuit. After each layer is applied, it is dried and fired. The firing temperature may be as low as 800° C or as high as 1450° C.

A complete circuit may require a number of successive screening and firing operations, as listed in Figure 17. A capacitor, for example, requires three superimposed layers: (1) conductor (electrode), (2) dielectric, and (3) conductor (electrode). Capacitors and resistors often are made slightly oversize and then trimmed mechanically by air abrasion, using a device like a dentist's drill or by machining if unusual precision is needed in their performance.

The thick-film process works on the principle that each functional material, whether a conductor, resistor, or dielectric, consists of flakes, or small particles, mixed with a finely ground glass. This mixture, in turn, is blended

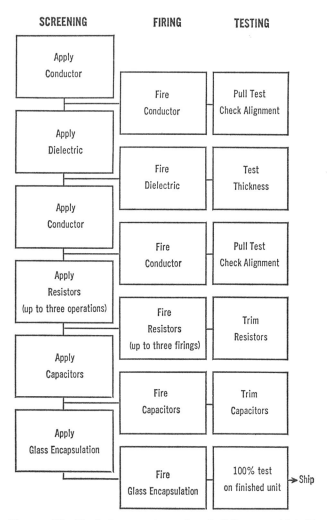

Figure 17. Typical procedure for building a thick-film microcircuit.

with a liquid and a temporary binder to form a thick paste about the consistency of paint. The paste is applied through the screen or mask which dictates *where* the material will go; it is deposited by a "squeegee" which controls *how thick* the coating will be. After the liquid has dried, the coating is fired. The finely ground glass, or frit, melts and serves to bond the particles of conductive, resistive, or capacitive material to each other and to the previous layer (or to the substrate, if this is the first layer). The technique is quite similar to the typical ceramic procedure of putting a vitreous, or porcelain, enamel coating on metal. Like enameling a bathtub, all the component layers are fused into a solid, compact structure. The difference is that when we make the circuits, each layer generally has a different composition and serves a different purpose.

After the required layers of the basic circuit have been screened and fired, small transistors or other special components that cannot easily be screened may be inserted and spot-welded. Finally, the entire circuit is often encapsulated in a low-temperature glass or other protective coating.

Thick-film circuits are slightly larger than thin-film types, but they are still extremely small in comparison with conventional miniaturized circuits. For instance, a circuit with as many as 15 resistors, or 10 capacitors and 8 resistors, can be screened on a substrate less than ¼ inch square. Another circuit has 56 resistors ranging from 51 ohms to 9500 ohms in a component 1½ inches square. All the processing operations for thick-film circuits are carried out in air rather than in a vacuum or controlled atmosphere, and this means a considerably lower investment in machinery and equipment.

METALLIZING AND SEALING

Nearly every electronic ceramic device requires either the installation of metal electrodes (metallizing) or the joining of two unlike materials such as metal and glass or ceramic and glass (sealing). Although electrodes and seals may seem minor and inactive parts of the device, it is essential that they have good mechanical and electrical properties. Therefore, a great deal of technical work has gone into the development of materials and procedures suitable for these two manufacturing steps.

ELECTRODING

A common way to apply electrodes to ceramic capacitors and ferroelectric transducers is to cover the desired electrode area with a paint or paste consisting of a liquid (a rather volatile material such as turpentine, for example), temporary organic binders that burn off during firing, a finely powdered glass composition, and, most important, flakes of a conducting metal like silver. (These are ingredients of the so-called "air-fired silver pastes.")

The coating may be applied with a paint brush, by spraying, or by forcing it through a mask or screen. The paste is dried, then fired in a furnace with an air atmosphere at a temperature usually less than 1000° C. Many companies buy these pastes already made up and ready to apply. Different types, in which the only changes are in the composition of the bonding glass, are available. Such a variety is important, because the heat-expansion characteristics of the various electronic ceramics differ so greatly that no single glass could serve all of them.

Glass-bonded metal electrodes also are made with powdered gold or platinum replacing the silver. In addition, electrodes can be applied by sputtering or evaporation techniques. These give us thinner electrodes, which is sometimes desirable; they require more highly specialized equipment and this can increase costs, however. When a thicker electrode is needed and the manufacturer wishes to avoid the glass-bond approach, an additional thickness can be placed over the sputtered or evaporated film by electroplating.

SEALS

An important thing to remember about seals is that the materials to be joined must be compatible. Since one is attached to the other at a high temperature, it is necessary that both materials have the same thermal (heat) expansion characteristics so that they will cool equally. Otherwise, strains will develop during cooling and the seal may crack. This can occur during processing or at a later time.

Seals are generally classified as ceramic-metal, glass-metal, or glass-ceramic. In the United States, glass is considered a ceramic product; here a glass-ceramic seal is one in which a crystalline ceramic material is sealed to a noncrystalline ceramic glass. A number of ceramic-to-metal seals are seen in Plate 13.

It is imperative that seal materials stick to each other tightly. People in the business say that one material must "wet" the other. A certain amount of chemical reaction must take place between them at the temperature of sealing. But not too much. Generally, a "reaction layer" is formed between the two materials, and this layer has intermediate properties somewhere between those of the materials themselves. This is particularly true when we seal either a glassy ceramic or a crystalline oxidic ceramic to a metal.

Finally, if the expansion characteristics of the two materials to be joined vary by an unsafe margin, "graded seals" are used. A series of seals is designed, each one different from the others by a safe amount, but all trending in the same direction, so that a gradual rather than a sudden transition in characteristics is provided.

Such a graded seal can be quite complex, and here again we see the vast importance of selecting and tailoring the right materials. These must (1) be capable of sealing two unlike compositions together; (2) form an interface that will resist repeated temperature changes, vibrations, and mechanical shocks; (3) furnish a good electrical insulator or conductor, and (5) remain gas-tight or vacuum-tight during years of service.

SUPERCONDUCTING MATERIALS

Until a few years ago, superconductivity was little more than a scientific curiosity. Today it has important industrial and research uses, and its applications are growing.

A superconducting material is one which loses all its electrical resistance below (1) a critical temperature; (2) a critical magnetic field, and (3) a critical current density. Superconductivity in these materials is attributed to an electronic interaction that results in separation of "superconducting" electrons from normal "resistive" electrons. The superconducting electrons are then free to carry an electric current without scattering and without resistance. Despite a hypothesis that certain materials might have superconductivity at room temperature, nearly all the superconducting materials known at present are metals with critical temperatures below 20° Kelvin, or −253° C (−424° F).

There are certain rules of superconductivity which seem to be related to atomic sizes, valence electron arrangements, crystal structure, and microstructure. We will not attempt to explain these characteristics in this discussion.

Cooled to liquid helium temperatures (roughly −269° C or −451° F), metals such as lead, tin, and niobium lose their electrical resistance. Then, if an electrical current is introduced, it continues to flow in the cooled metal until the temperature is raised above the material's *superconducting transition temperature*. Superconductivity has been observed in at least one semiconductor, germanium telluride (GeTe), when strongly polycrystalline, sintered samples were tested.

The ceramist's interest in superconductivity is aroused by the fact that a complete loss of electrical resistivity has been found in strontium titanate, a well-known composition used in electronic ceramics. Heated in a vacuum or in hydrogen at temperatures between 700° and 1200° C, the strontium titanate became an oxide semiconductor. Later the processed material became superconducting when cooled to 0.25° K ($-272.9°$ C or $-459.2°$ F). The investigators discovered that the material was a "hard" superconductor, belonging to a class of substances that retain their zero resistance in abnormally high external magnetic fields.

The present and planned uses of superconductivity are naturally those that can take advantage of the absence of electrical resistance. The leading applications seem to be in the development of magnetic fields for use in research, especially in providing intense, steady-state fields in large volume. The advantages offered by a cryogenic magnet are suggested by the following illustration: A conventional 100,000-gauss magnet requires 1.7 million watts of electrical energy and 1000 gpm of water for cooling. With superconductors, the same field strength is produced by 300 watts, and the cryogenic environment is maintained by a 10,000-watt refrigerator. (Cryogenics is the branch of physics that deals with very low temperatures.)

Among the cryogenic devices in use or under consideration, in addition to high-strength magnets, are computer elements, gyroscopes, frictionless motors, low-loss coaxial cables, superconducting transmission lines, and extremely sensitive electrical instruments and electronic circuits. Cryogenic coils are proposed as a means of storing very large amounts of energy.

In these devices, how can we use a brittle or powdery oxidic material like strontium titanate? The "wires" for cryogenic electromagnets are produced by filling a hollow metal tubing with the superconducting material, whether it be oxidic or a metal alloy. These conductors look much like the tubing used in heating units of an electric range. For example, a zero-resistance coil can be prepared by stuffing the tubing with powdered Nb_3Sn (or a mixture of powdered niobium and powdered tin), compacting the mixture, and reacting the metals in place. This produces a continuous superconducting path inside the length of tubing. The coil must be cooled drastically, however, before it loses all electrical resistance.

PHOTOCONDUCTIVE AND ELECTROLUMINESCENT MATERIALS

Photoconductive materials undergo a change in electrical resistivity when visible or infra-red light shines on

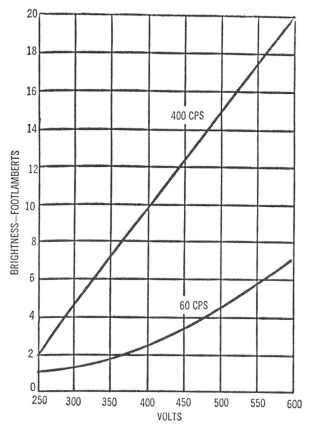

Figure 18. Brightness vs. lamp voltage for a 600-volt electroluminescent device. Note also how increasing the excitation frequency raises the brightness.

them. A similar group known as electroluminescent materials emit light when placed in an electric field. The photoconductors can be used to turn on street lights when it becomes dark, for example, no matter what the hour. They can also trigger a mechanism that opens a door when you approach it with your car headlights burning—or when you interrupt the light beam of an "electric eye" as at an airport or railroad station.

Electroluminescent materials make possible "light panels"—large areas of wall or ceiling that glow with a uniform light. These lights are not based on the principle of a glowing filament, as in the incandescent bulb, or on that of an electrically excited gas giving energy to a "phosphor powder," as in the fluorescent tube. (A phosphor is a material capable of absorbing energy of a wavelength that the eye does not see readily, and emitting that energy at a different wavelength—in the visible range.) Instead, the electroluminescent material directly converts an electric current into light without any intermediate mechanism. (Some relationships between brightness, frequency, and voltage are seen in Figure 18.)

PHOTOCONDUCTIVE MATERIALS

Specially prepared materials such as lead sulphide (PbS) and solid solutions of cadmium sulphide and cadmium selenide are used for making photoconductor elements. One patent, for example, describes a photosensitive photoconductor device containing a crystallization product having the generalized composition AB_2X_4, in which A is zinc or cadmium, B is indium, gallium, and/or aluminum, and X is sulphur, selenium, and/or tellurium. The device is activated by 10^{-5} to 10^{-2} atoms of gold, silver, or copper incorporated per molecule of the composition. (The activating materials are carefully included when the photoconductive material is being synthesized.)

ELECTROLUMINESCENT MATERIALS

Electroluminescence (EL) has made possible the commercial development of a new type of light source. EL is different from anything previously known in two respects: (1) the light is "cold," that is, it is not dependent on a heated source, and (2) it can originate from a rather large area rather than from a filament or tube.

The device is one in which light is given off from a crystalline phosphor placed in a thin layer between two closely spaced electrodes of an electrical capacitor. One of the electrodes must be transparent. Light output varies with applied voltage and is strongly dependent on the frequency of the alternating current used. The efficiency of this light source and the color of the light produced are determined chiefly by the characteristics of the phosphor.

The crystal composition most frequently used for generating light by electroluminescence is zinc sulphide (ZnS). Tailoring of this material to produce variations in the light's color and to modify other characteristics is done by partial substitutions—cadmium for zinc and selenium for sulphur. Also essential is the addition of small amounts (from 0.0001 to 0.1 percent) of specific metals as "activators." Copper, silver, and gold are generally chosen for this purpose. Similarly, "coactivators" may be used; these may include a halogen (principally chlorine); a three-valent material such as aluminum, gallium, or indium; and the rare earth elements.

Phosphors made with zinc sulphide have been used for a number of years in the screens of oscilloscopes, radars, and TV picture tubes. They generate an image when struck by an electron beam, but this effect is not to be confused with electroluminescence. Still other phosphors composed of silicates and phosphates are employed on the inner walls of fluorescent lamps. These materials respond more efficiently than zinc sulphide to the particular wavelength of the "exciting radiation" of fluorescent lamps.

EL LAMPS

In addition to their other unique features, electroluminescent lamps do not fail suddenly and unexpectedly in the way a filament lamp "burns out." EL lamps are popular in night lights; switch plates; clock faces; telephone, radio, and TV dials; automobile instrument panels; highway signs and markers; and decorative panels in a variety of colors for walls, ceilings, and other areas. The level of illumination so far is moderately low.

Three types of EL lamps are in use: metal-ceramic, glass-ceramic, and flexible plastic. A typical five-layer metal-ceramic construction is shown in Figure 19. This

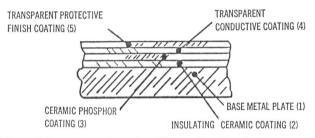

TRANSPARENT PROTECTIVE FINISH COATING (5)

TRANSPARENT CONDUCTIVE COATING (4)

CERAMIC PHOSPHOR COATING (3)

BASE METAL PLATE (1)

INSULATING CERAMIC COATING (2)

Figure 19. Cross-section view illustrating the five-layer construction of a metal-ceramic electroluminescent lamp (area light source).

can be considered a special porcelain enamel composite. As seen in the illustration, a metal panel, layer No. 1, usually iron or steel, is coated successively with an electrically insulating ground coat (No. 2), a phosphor-containing cover coat (No. 3), a clear overglaze electrode (No. 4), and a clear protective layer (No. 5).

These coatings are fired in place as with conventional porcelain enamels. The metal provides one electrode of the capacitor, while a second, transparent electrode is formed by spraying a conducting tin-oxide layer over the thin glass layer (No. 4) that covers the phosphor-containing coat. This conducting layer, in turn, usually is covered with a second clear-glass layer (No. 5) for mechanical and electrical protection and to prevent penetration by moisture.

Glass-ceramic construction is similar to the metal-ceramic makeup. Flexible lamps are made by using a thin metal foil such as aluminum for the first electrode. This is covered with a thin uniform coating of white, high-dielectric material followed by a mixture of phosphor with a high-dielectric organic material. The mixture is converted to a tough plastic film by heating at relatively low temperatures. The second electrode, which is also the light-emitting side of the capacitor (lamp), consists of a thin conducting glass "paper" cemented to the phosphor layer. The entire unit is sealed in a protective envelope.

This type of construction is suitable for making lamps in long strips, in widths up to eight or twelve inches. A commercial version of the strip approach is called "Tape Light." The tape is 1¾ inches wide and comes in various colors including green, blue, white, and yellow.

THERMOELECTRIC GENERATORS

Thermoelectric generators are electronic devices that have the ability to convert heat (or, more precisely, a difference in temperature) directly into electricity. Thus, they produce electricity without the use of an intermediate device such as a conventional generator; no moving parts are needed to generate electrical power by this method.

The basic principles of thermoelectric generation have been known for more than one hundred years. In an electrical circuit consisting of two dissimilar conductors, if one junction is placed in a heat reservoir at a temperature different from the other, a current will flow in the circuit. The current is due to the fact that heat is absorbed at the hot junction and rejected at the cold junction. This effect—known as the *Seebeck potential*—is the basis of the thermocouple, a temperature-measuring device.

Two unlike wires—for example, one of platinum and the other of platinum with 10 percent rhodium—will generate a voltage, an electromotive force (emf) proportional to the difference in temperature between the hot and cold junctions. By measuring the temperature of the cold junction, we can tell (from a temperature-voltage calibration) what the temperature is at the other (hot) junction—inside a furnace, for instance.

This Seebeck effect is the basis of the thermoelectric power generator. The efficiency of such a generator is not high, but it is a useful source of electric power under certain conditions—as when an available source of heat would otherwise be wasted, such as inside a space probe or in a small nuclear power plant at a remote unattended weather station.

An opposite effect also can be put to work. A battery inserted in a circuit of dissimilar conductors causes current to flow through the junctions. Heat is absorbed at one junction, causing it to cool; meanwhile, heat is rejected at the other junction. This temperature gradient obtained by application of an electric field to a junction is known as the *Peltier effect*.

THERMOELECTRIC MATERIALS

The Russians are given credit for the first practical demonstration of the generation of electricity directly from heat, using thermoelectric materials. A small thermoelectric generator in the shape of a doughnut was fitted over the chimney of a kerosene lamp, and the heat from the chimney was converted into enough electricity to power a radio set. Thus it was shown that a family or community miles from an electric system or from a drugstore where batteries are sold can still have good radio reception as well as a certain amount of illumination.

Here's another application of thermoelectric materials: They can be used for "electric cooling," sometimes called "Peltier effect cooling"—not the way the typical home refrigerator works, with electric motor and compressor, but directly, simply, and silently. This new cool-

ing is excellent for noiseless air-conditioning and refrigeration in deep-dive submarines, for example, and for
cooling small, critical areas of an electronic circuit without having to air-condition the whole piece of equipment.

As with so many other electronic applications, materials are the key to success in thermoelectric devices.
Without the proper materials, in fact, results are almost
negligible. Most promising in this field are compounds
resulting from combinations of elements from groups
II-V, II-VI, and V-VI of the periodic table. The best of
the lot for power generation appear to be lead telluride
(PbTe) and silicon-germanium alloys, and for refrigeration, bismuth telluride (Bi_2Te_3) and solid solution
alloys of bismuth, antimony, tellurium, and selenium
$(Bi,Sb)_2(Te,Se)_3$. A typical example of a thermoelectric
power generator is a small unit—without moving parts,
thus quiet and simple—generating 500 watts at about 10
percent efficiency when the hot temperature is 875° C
and the cold junction is 35° C. This generator is equipped
with a silicon-germanium alloy.

A ceramic thermoelectric generator using only oxides,
but with platinum electrodes and conductors, is pictured
in Plate 14. The generator shown in the illustration can
be operated at temperatures up to 2400° F (1310° C).
Even the nuts and bolts that hold the unit together are
made of a ceramic composition; this is for good electrical insulation and to help the generator withstand the
heat.

How cold is thermoelectric cooling? A thermoelectric
junction of the general composition $(Bi,Sb)_2(Te,Se)_3$
can be 78° C colder than its hot junction when the latter
is at 25° C. In other words, we can electrically generate
cooling from room temperature to about −63° F.

TUBES VS. TRANSISTORS

There is a popular notion that transistors will soon
replace vacuum tubes; this is due in part to our natural
enthusiasm for new discoveries. Indeed, transistors will
take over *some* of the duties previously monopolized by

tubes, and there will be certain areas where either tubes or transistors may serve equally well. But the fact is, there are many other fields where tubes are still preferred and will continue to be chosen. The advantages and disadvantages of these devices in several application areas are given below.

(a) Power Requirements

In cases where the available power input is limited and high power output is not required, transistors are the logical choice. For example, in hearing aids, portable radios, and space vehicles, all of which are generally supplied with battery power, the low drain and high efficiency of transistors spell the difference. An automobile radio using a direct-current source is also a good place for transistors. On the other hand, if the equipment is to be operated with alternating current, other considerations may favor tubes over transistors.

(b) Ambient Temperature

Semiconductors (the materials in transistors) are far more sensitive to changes in temperature than are vacuum tubes. Germanium and silicon show a considerable variation in properties with changes in temperature. Their top operating temperatures seem to be around 100° and 200° C, respectively. Vacuum tubes with glass envelopes can operate well above 200° C; in fact, the ceramic tube (described in Chapter VII) can go over 400° C with practically no difference in characteristics. Consequently, the use of transistors in places where the temperature of the environment, or ambient temperature, varies widely requires a great deal of attention to temperature-compensating elements and circuit modifications.

(c) Frequency and Noise

When the frequency of transistors goes above 500 kilocycles, certain fundamental problems have been noted. These indicate that such characteristics as barrier thickness, area, and carrier mobility of transistors are somehow related to capacitance, gain, and power-handling ability (heat dissipation). For this reason, tubes still are preferred for very-high-frequency (VHF) and ultra-high-frequency (UHF) applications—in television transmitters and receivers, for example.

Transistors are free of hum and microphonics, however, which makes them particularly useful for audio pre-amplifiers. Tubes, on the other hand, are more suited for wide-band amplifiers in radar and television equipment. The ceramic tube seems to be preferred over the best transistor for ultra-low-frequency flicker noise.

(d) Nuclear Radiation

Available unclassified data show that transistors are vulnerable to high-energy gamma radiation, which does not affect tubes to any measureable degree. Reports indicate that with bombardment by both thermal and fast neutrons, glass tubes last a hundred times longer and ceramic tubes about a thousand times longer than transistors. This factor can be vital in certain military applications.

(e) Size and Weight

The tiny transistors have an obvious advantage over conventional vacuum tubes insofar as physical size is concerned, although this is not necessarily true with ceramic tubes. In the case of power transistors, the added dimensions and weight of the heat sink and radiator must be included in the over-all determination of relative merits of the two types of devices.

Chapter X

A LOOK AT THE FUTURE

All the signs indicate a continued explosive growth for electronic ceramics, and some of the areas to watch are the following:

(a) Semiconductors

As we have seen, the demand for semiconductors (transistors and rectifiers) is doubling and even tripling annually. The makers of such devices as capacitors, resistors, and similar circuit components have found that their older products—for example, the ceramic-based capacitors and resistors of the vacuum tube circuit—are not compatible with the semiconductors, which operate on extremely low voltages in comparison with vacuum tubes. The former were built to operate in circuits that might have plate voltages as high as 90 or 135 volts (your parents may remember the 45-volt B-batteries of the early portable sets), whereas the latter are designed chiefly for circuits using 1½ to 4½ volts.

In order to keep pace, manufacturers of electronic devices and equipment have had to design completely new lines of products to go along with the modern types of semiconductors and circuits. Stereo radios and record players are now on the market featuring "solid-state" circuits which use recently introduced electronic-ceramic components.

(b) Miniaturization and Microminiaturization

Thin-film and thick-film circuits appear destined to maintain their vigorous upsurge. The vacuum deposition of components through masks or the screening and firing of successive layers of electronic components in a procedure closely resembling porcelain-enameling (as described in Chapter IX) may eventually replace earlier types of circuitry, but at present all types of miniaturization and microminiaturization are in active demand. For special applications such as space exploration and in situations requiring unusual industrial controls, the so-called thick-film or monolithic circuits may be increasingly used due to their small size and ruggedness.

(c) Industrial Controls

We can safely predict a further expansion of automation, industrial controls, and industrial programming. A good example of what is happening in this field is seen in Japan, where high-speed trains are controlled electronically from a headquarters, and the motorman has relatively little to do. In the San Francisco Bay area, rapid transit trains that may be operated almost entirely by electronic means are being studied. In transportation, communications, and manufacturing, the increasing use of electronic controls will, of course, bring greater demands for new ceramic devices and circuits.

(d) Microwave Communication

The use of microwave communication is burgeoning for such things as voice, television, computer data, press copy, and electronic-facsimile duplication. Meanwhile, we see a parallel growth in the necessary ferrites and dielectric materials for wave guides, controls, and switching.

(e) Electronics in Navigation

The military probably will increase its use of radar. Commercial aviation is putting larger amounts of radar equipment into service, and private planes are being equipped with radar devices. Electronic gear for traffic control, landing aids, and for similar purposes will eventually be standard equipment at the smaller as well as the larger airports.

Most of our larger seagoing vessels now have sonar navigational aids, including depth finders. Smaller private boats also are being equipped with fathometers, ship-to-shore communication links, direction finders, and other electronic devices.

(f) Radiation-Tolerant Materials

The growing use of nuclear energy for power generation means greater requirements for sensing devices and control circuits. Many of the electronic components used in and near these nuclear reactors must be able to resist damage by radiation. Some devices, in fact, will have to be able to withstand elevated temperatures as well as high radiation levels. Thus, ceramic materials are bound to be a popular choice in this area.

(g) Space Technology

Ceramic materials are vital to the success of space missions, and it is anticipated that many of the electronic-ceramic devices built to control space hardware will find applications in our daily lives. This has not taken place to a significant extent as yet, however.

(h) Computers

Electronic data-processing machines are the only known solution to the mountains of paperwork that plague today's style of living. Sales of computers leaped from essentially zero in 1952 to 350 million dollars in 1956; they reached some two billion dollars in 1965 and are expected to exceed seven billion dollars in 1969.

Not only have total sales skyrocketed, but the variety of specialized computers has grown, and new applications are reported almost daily. The speed of computers is increasing at a fantastic rate. We once spoke of operations that took seconds; then came machines capable of doing complex tasks in a few milliseconds (thousandths of a second). Now the microsecond (millionth of a second) seems a rather long time, and we find that the nanosecond (billionth of a second) is not an uncommon time unit in the newest computers.

These devices have reduced the time required for handling vast quantities of paperwork from weeks and months to a matter of days and even hours. But what is more important, they are providing answers to complex problems that previously could not be solved in any reasonable length of time. As we saw in Chapter V, ceramic memory cores are playing an important role in today's computers.

SUMMARY

I had two goals in mind when writing this book. The chief objective was to describe electronic ceramics. These new ceramic materials have many properties so very different from those that have been associated with ceramic materials from the dawn of history that they call for a new understanding of the nature, scope, and future of the field of ceramics. I hope that these chapters have contributed in that respect.

The second goal was to provide an insight, although a limited and one-sided one, into what is steadily growing to be one of the more significant scientific and engineering activities of our time: the systematic and planned discovery, improvement, and manufacture of special materials for special purposes. As you have learned, this operation commonly is referred to as the "tailoring" of materials. Technical demands are changing almost daily, and new and improved materials are continually needed to keep pace with the advancing thrust of new requirements.

In my enthusiasm for telling you about electronic ceramics, I hope I did not give you the impression that they are on their way toward overshadowing the conventional ceramics. It just happens that, by comparison, some of the newer developments in electronic ceramics appear to be more spectacular and more unexpected than perhaps equally significant advances in the older product fields.

Likewise, in my eagerness to show you how the ceramic scientist and the ceramic engineer go about the job of tailoring electronic ceramics when they find it necessary to do so, I did not point out that ceramists in the other field of ceramics also apply scientific facts and improved industrial controls to develop and produce new modifications of their products. It is likely that one would have to select very different aspects of chemistry, physics, mineralogy, and engineering to describe the particular combinations of facts and principles made use of in tailoring such diverse materials as dinnerware, enameled steel, refractories, glass, and structural ceramics. And yet, largely the same college curriculum should help equip one to engage in any or all of these fields.

SELECTED FURTHER READING
IN CERAMICS

Ceramic Fabrication Processes, by W. D. Kingery. New York: John Wiley & Sons (1958).

Ceramic Glazes, 2nd ed., by C. W. Parmelee. Chicago: Industrial Publications (1949).

Ceramics for the Artist Potter, by F. H. Norton. Reading, Massachusetts: Addison-Wesley Publishing Company (1956).

Ceramics in the Modern World, by Maurice Chandler. New York: Doubleday & Company, Inc. (1968).

Ceramics: Stone Age to Space Age, by Lane Mitchell. New York: Scholastic Book Services Division, Scholastic Magazines (1963).

Earth and Fire, by S. R. Scholes. Alfred, New York: State University of New York at Alfred University, College of Ceramics (1960).

Glass, the Miracle Maker, 2nd ed., by C. J. Phillips. New York: Pitman Publishing Corporation (1948).

Introduction to Ceramics, by W. D. Kingery. New York: John Wiley & Sons (1960).

Porcelain Enamels, by A. I. Andrews. Champaign, Illinois: Garrard Press (1961).

Refractories, 3rd ed., by F. H. Norton. New York: McGraw-Hill Book Company (1950).

GLOSSARY

Abrasive. A substance for removing material by grinding, lapping, polishing, etc.

Absorption. The relation of the water absorbed by a ceramic specimen to the weight of the dry specimen, expressed in percent.

Amorphous. Without definite form. In ceramics, chemistry, and mineralogy, not crystalline.

Angstrom unit (AU). One-hundred-millionth of a centimeter. A unit used in measuring the length of light waves, the sizes of atoms and molecules, and other small dimensions.

Anion. A negative ion.

Bias voltage. A fixed voltage applied to the electrodes of an electronic device, usually for control purposes.

Body. The structural portion of a ceramic article, or the material or mixture from which it is made.

Burn. The heat treatment to which a ceramic material is subjected in the firing process.

Calcine. To heat a ceramic mixture to less than fusion, for use as a constituent in a ceramic composition. The product of such heat treatment.

Capacitor. A device consisting of conducting plates, or electrodes, separated by a dielectric and used for the storage of electrical charge.

Cation. A positive ion.

Cermet. A nonhomogeneous body composed of two or more intimately mixed but separable phases, at least one of which is metallic and the other ceramic.

Clay. A natural mineral aggregate consisting essentially of hydrous aluminum silicates; plastic when wetted, rigid when dried, and hard and rocklike when fired to a sufficiently high temperature.

Crystal. A solidified form of substance in which the atoms or molecules are arranged in a definite and repeating pattern.

Crystallite. A very small crystalline formation.

Crystallographic. Related to the properties and performance of a material resulting from its characteristic crystal structure.

Curie temperature. Broadly, the temperature above which a magnetic material becomes paramagnetic (loses its magnetism) or the temperature above which a ferroelectric material becomes paraelectric (loses its spontaneous polarization).

Delay line. An electronic device for the purpose of temporarily detaining or storing an electrical signal.

Density. The ratio of the mass of an object to its volume, commonly expressed in grams per cubic centimeter.

Devitrification. Crystallization in or of a glass.

Dielectric. A medium in which it is possible to produce and maintain an electric field with little or no further supply of energy from outside sources.

Dielectric constant. The ratio of the capacitance of a dielectric material equipped with electrodes and the capacitance of the same electrode system with only vacuum between the conducting plates.

Dielectric strength. The maximum voltage per unit thickness that a dielectric can withstand before it breaks or a conducting path is formed through it; commonly expressed in volts per mil.

Dipole. Two equal and opposite electric charges or magnetic poles separated from each other, that is, not superimposed.

Domain. An area or region in a crystal or polycrystalline material in which the ferroelectric dipoles or magnetic moments are aligned in a common direction.

Electrodes. The conducting terminals by which connections are made to an electric source or to an electronic component.

Electroluminescent. Having the property of emitting light when excited with an electric field.

Electromechanical. Having the characteristics of converting electrical energy into mechanical energy, or the reverse.

Electrostriction. The mechanical distortion or dimensional change in a dielectric material when an electric field is applied to it.

Enamel. A glassy, opaque, ornamental or protective coating fused to the surfaces of metal, glass, pottery, etc.

Encapsulation. A material or materials used to encase or package an electronic component, device, or circuit intimately, to provide protection against moisture, dirt, vibration, impact, and the like.

Envelope. A covering for the protection or electrical isolation of an electronic component or device as, for example, the glass or ceramic envelope of a vacuum tube.

Feldspar. A mineral aggregate consisting chiefly of sodium, potassium, or calcium aluminum silicates, commonly used as a flux in ceramic bodies.

Ferrite. In electronic ceramics, any of various compounds of iron oxide combined with other oxides and usually having pronounced magnetic properties.

Ferroelectricity. The phenomenon exhibited by those materials which in some temperature range show spontaneous alignment of electric dipoles, the direction of which can be changed by an external electrostatic field.

Filter. A device or substance allowing electric signals (currents) of certain frequencies or frequency ranges to pass while preventing the passage of others.

Firing. The controlled heat treatment of ceramicware in a furnace or kiln in order to harden or glaze the material.

Flint (pottery flint). A finely powdered form of silica (SiO_2) used as a raw material in many ceramic compositions.

Flux. A substance that promotes fusion in a ceramic mixture.

Gauss. A unit used in measuring the magnetic induction resulting when a material is subjected to a magnetic field.

Glass. An inorganic product of fusion that has cooled to a rigid condition without crystallizing.

Glass ceramic. A glass composition, or an article made of it, specially designed for conversion to a polycrystalline condition by controlled nucleation and crystallization.

Glaze. A thin, glassy, ceramic coating fired on a formed ceramic article, or the mixture from which the coating is made.

Grain. A small, hard particle, as of sand or other inorganic materials.

Hysteresis. A lag in the effect in a body when the force acting on it is changed. Thus, a lag in the change in magnetization on varying the magnetic field or the lag in the changing polarization of a ferroelectric on varying the applied electric field.

Impervious. The degree of densification of an electronic ceramic implying complete resistance to the penetration of moisture.

Insulator. A device, commonly of glass or porcelain, used to prevent the passage or leakage of electricity.

Inversion. In crystallography, a reversible physical change to another form, due to a change in conditions such as temperature or pressure.

Isomorphism. The identity or very close similarity of the crystal forms of two or more different chemical compositions.

Kiln. A type of furnace used for firing ceramic wares.

Linear. In electronic devices, the characteristic of having essentially a straight-line relationship between an applied force and the resulting response.

Magnetic field. Magnetic forces, as between the poles of a magnet.

Magnetic permeability. The property of a magnetic material that determines the degree to which it modifies the magnetic flux in the region occupied by the material in a magnetic field.

Maturing temperature. The temperature at which a material must be held for a selected length of time in order to develop the desired properties.

Micron (micro-meter). One-millionth of a meter, one-thousandth of a millimeter, 0.0000394 inch.

Microstructure. The arrangement and interrelations of crystal and grain sizes and the orientation and packing of the phases in a material.

Microwave. An extremely short (high-frequency) electromagnetic wave.

Mineral. A chemical element or inorganic compound occurring naturally in the earth and having a distinctive and consistent set of physical properties such as color, hardness, and crystal structure.

Nonlinear. Having a variable, rather than a straight-line, relationship between applied forces and properties (response).

Nucleating agent. A material serving to promote the formation of, or serving as, the nuclei on which crystallization takes place in the devitrification of a glass.

Oersted. A unit of magnetic intensity. The intensity of magnetic field in a vacuum in which a unit magnetic pole experiences a mechanical force of one dyne in the direction of the field.

Phosphor. A substance that gives off light when subjected to radiation or when otherwise excited.

Photoconductor. A substance that conducts electricity when excited with light.

Piezoelectricity. The phenomenon whereby certain substances generate electrical charges when subjected to mechanical deformation, including that resulting from vibration or from pressure change.

Polarize. To form dipoles.

Polycrystalline. Consisting of many crystals; not single-crystal.

Polymorphism. The ability of a substance to exist in more than one crystal form.

Porosity. The percentage of the total volume of a material occupied by pores.

Pyrometry. The measurement of temperatures.

Rectifier. A device for changing alternating current into direct current.

Refractories. Materials used to withstand high temperatures.

Resistance (electrical). The property of opposing the passage of an electric current.

Resistor. A component used in an electrical circuit primarily to provide resistance.

Resonance absorption. If the frequencies of two systems are nearly equal, energy can easily be transferred between the systems, which are said to be in resonance. Resonance absorption is a factor in the use of certain ferrites at microwave frequencies.

Sinter. To bring about the formation of a coherent mass by heating a ceramic material or mixture to less than the temperature at which complete melting takes place.

Solid solution. A homogeneous molecular mixture in solid form.

Sonar. Apparatus that transmits sound waves in the water and receives the vibrations echoed from an object; used in detecting submarines, locating schools of fish, measuring the depth of waters, etc.

Stoichiometry. The numerical relationships, usually simple, of elements combining into compounds. For example, the stoichiometric ratio of hydrogen to oxygen in water is 2 to 1 (H_2O).

Structure. The arrangement and interrelationship of the parts to the whole, such as the arrangements of the atoms in a crystal, or the arrangements of the crystals in a rock or manufactured material.

Synthetic. A material produced by chemical reaction, rather than of natural origin.

System. A set of things so related as to form a unity or whole. Commonly used to designate a group of chemicals considered as a unity, such as "ferrites in the MnO-ZnO-Fe_2O_3 system."

Thermal conductivity. The ability of a material to conduct heat. The rate of heat flow, under steady conditions, through unit area, per unit temperature gradient in the direction perpendicular to the area.

Thermal expansion. The characteristic change in dimensions occurring in a material when it is heated.

Thermistor. A device made with a material having a large change in resistance for a small change in temperature, and therefore used for measuring temperatures.

Thermocouple. A pair of wires of unlike composition joined (coupled) for the purpose of measuring differences in temperature.

Thermoelectric. Having to do with electricity produced directly from heat (or, more properly, from a difference in temperatures).

Toroid. A ringlike solid. This term is employed widely to designate small units of ferrite used industrially.

Transducer. Broadly, any device that carries energy from one system into another. A telephone receiver is a form of transducer. It converts the electrical energy in the wire into acoustical (sound) energy in the air. In ceramic electromechanical transducers, the ferroelectric material directly converts electrical signals into sound waves, or vice versa.

Transistor. A very small electronic device, functioning much as a vacuum tube, but controlling the flow of current without the use of a vacuum by utilizing the peculiar conductive properties of such materials as silicon and germanium.

Transition temperature. The temperature at which a material passes from one condition, state, or form to another.

Ultrasonic. Operating in frequencies beyond the range of sound waves.

Valence. The capacity of an element (ion) to combine with or replace another, measured in terms of hydrogen as one. Oxygen has a valence of two, that is, one atom of oxygen combines with two atoms of hydrogen. This fact can be presented also in an ionic equation: $2H^+ + O^{2-} = H_2O$.

Varistor. A nonlinear device in which the resistance changes markedly in response to a change in the applied electrical voltage.

Vitreous. Glasslike, commonly as evidenced by low water absorption.

Vitrified. Made glassy by fusion due to heat.

INDEX

Abrasives, 38, 140
Absorption, 19, 140
Accelerators, ferrites in, 54
Alumel in thermocouples, 16
Alumina, 18, 24, 93, 101–3, 105
Aluminum phosphate, 39–41
Angstrom units, 41–42, 140
Antiferroelectric material, 74
Antiferromagnetic material, 63
Atomic sizes, 41–42

Ball-milling, 60
Barium ferrites, 53
Barium titanate, 23, 28, 29, 45,
    82, 104
  as capacitor material, 93–99
  ferroelectric behavior of, 79
  perovskite structure of, 72–74
Bell, Alexander Graham, 2
Berlinite, quartz compared to,
    40–41
Beryllia, 93, 101–3
Beryllium fluoride, 45–46
Biasing voltage, 98
Bismuth stannate, 99
Bismuth telluride, 130
Bleininger, A. V., 35
Body, defined, 10, 140
Boettger, C. F., 33
Bond strengths, 43–45
Bone china, 33
Boron nitride, 101
Bragg, W. L., 41
Brookhaven National Labora-
    tory, 54

Cadmium niobate, 24, 71
Cadmium sulphide, 125
Capacitance
  electrostatic, 90
  temperature coefficient of,
    96–97
Capacitive ceramics, 23
Capacitors, 89–106

ceramic disc, 91
defined, 23, 140
development of, 92–95
electroding of, 120
glass for, 108–9
Carbon filament, invention of,
    1–2
Carbon granule microphone,
    invention of, 2
Ceramic engineers, 32, 48
Ceramic scientists, 32, 47–48
Ceramics
  defined, 5, 9
  first college program in, 34
  history of, 33–34
  metals compared to, 7–9
  See also Electronic ceramics;
    other specific topics
Cermets, 25–26, 140
Chromel in thermocouples, 16
Chromites, 61
Clay, 12, 140
Coercive field, 77
Communication filters, 80
Components. *See* Electronic
    components
Computers, 135–36
  ferrites in, 52–53
Condensers, 90
  variable, 92
Conducting glasses, 111–12
Constantan in thermocouples,
    16
Coordination numbers, 42–43
Copper stannate, 99
Copper in thermocouples, 16
Coprecipitating, 60
Cordierite, 93, 101, 102
Corning Glass Works, 107, 109,
    110
Cristobalite, 36, 39, 40
Cryogenic devices, 123
Crystal chemistry, 37–46
  model structures in, 45–46

Vacuum tubes
  "all-ceramic," 102–3
  miniaturization of, 2–3
  spacers of alumina in, 24, 102
  transistors vs., 130–32
Vanadium pentoxide, 112
Van der Waal's bonds, 44
Varistors, 103–4, 146
Vibration detectors, 24
Vitreous, defined, 10, 146
Vitrification, 14, 27

Voltage gradient, 91

Wedgwood, Josiah, 33
Windshields, 112

X-ray tubes, 112

Yttrium-iron garnet (YIG), 60

Zinc sulphide, 126
Zircon, 93, 101, 102

PORTSMOUTH POLYTECHNIC LIBRARY

PORTSMOUTH
POLYTECHNIC
LIBRARY